CHEMICAL PHYSICS OF SEMICONDUCTORS

THE VAN NOSTRAND
SERIES IN PHYSICAL CHEMISTRY

Edited by

T. M. SUGDEN, F.R.S.

Research Director, Shell Research Ltd.,

Thornton Research Centre, Chester

This series aims to provide a group of fundamental books covering the whole field of physical chemistry. It will be the aim of each volume to summarize its topic in a modern fashion for senior honours undergraduates and postgraduates, and for all practising chemists whether engaged in industry, teaching or research.

P. G. ASHMORE—*Kinetics of Chemical Reactions*

N. BASCO—*Photochemistry*

P. M. GUNDRY—*Heterogeneous Catalysis*

G. KOHNSTAM—*Mechanisms of Reactions in Solutions*

M. LEFORT—*Nuclear Chemistry*

F. M. PAGE—*Ionization in Flames*

M. STEINBERG—*Introductory Solid State Chemistry*

J. P. SUCHET—*Chemical Physics of Semiconductors*

T. M. SUGDEN and C. N. KENNEY—*Microwave Spectroscopy*

Additional titles will be listed and announced as published

Chemical Physics of Semiconductors

by

J. P. SUCHET

Centre National de la Recherche Scientifique
Institut de Magnétisme et de Physique
du Solide, Bellevue/Meudon (Seine-et-Oise)

translated by

E. HEASELL

Department of Electrical Engineering
Imperial College of Science and Technology
London

D. VAN NOSTRAND COMPANY LTD
LONDON
TORONTO   NEW YORK
PRINCETON, NEW JERSEY

D. VAN NOSTRAND COMPANY LTD.
358 Kensington High Street, London, W.14

D. VAN NOSTRAND COMPANY INC.
120 Alexander Street, Princeton, New Jersey
24 West 40 Street, New York 18

D. VAN NOSTRAND COMPANY (CANADA) LTD.
25 Hollinger Road, Toronto 16

A revised and enlarged translation of *Chimie physique des semiconducteurs*,
published by Dunod, Paris, 1962

This book has been published in Russian by
Izdatelstvo Metallurgiya, Moscow (1964)
and will be published in Polish by
Panstwowe Wydawnictwo Naukowe, Warsaw

Library of Congress Catalog Card No. 64–22289

Printed in Great Britain by
Butler & Tanner Ltd., Frome and London

PREFACE

THE growing interest shown in compound semiconductors and the need to give an account of their properties within the framework of a general theory taking into consideration their chemical bonds, explains the appearance of this book in the Soviet Union, and in Great Britain and the United States. I am happy to recall that such development had been fore seen by the late Academician A. F. Ioffe, for whom, as early as 1951, semiconductivity was essentially related to short range order. It is also fair to mention the turning point in 1955 marked by the work of Reiss, Fuller and Morin, at the Bell Telephone Laboratories, on the equilibrium reactions between defects and impurities in crystals.

Certain modifications have been made to the original text. Apart from the correction of minor errors, Chapter 6 has been completely re-modelled and now brings together in a condensed form the old Chapters 6 and 7 of the French edition. Chapters 7 and 8 have been specially added, and take account of my past two years' work. The former sets out, in a more lucid fashion, the method of approach that I propose to call the 'crystallo-chemical model'. This model also serves to give a more rigorous expression to the ideas of other research workers, notably those of my colleague Goodman in Great Britain on ionicity, and those of my colleague Folberth in the German Federal Republic on polarization. Chapter 8 establishes the relationship to magnetism, and the presence of this section seemed necessary because of the growing importance of semiconducting compounds which contain transition elements. It explains in a simple way the magnetic interactions that occur in these crystals.

I hope that the slightly novel point of view from which I have approached the chemical physics of semiconductors will assist research workers in all countries to perceive the relations that exist between different fields wrongly considered as independent from one another. The appreciation of such connections is often very fruitful.

I wish to thank M. Charles Guillaud, Directeur d'Institut de Recherches,

M. Michel Rodot, Directeur de Recherches, and all my colleagues at the Centre National de la Recherche Scientifique for the interest and the part that they have taken in this work.

I should like to thank Dr. T. M. Sugden and Dr. E. Heasell for the numerous suggestions they have made to improve the presentation of the English edition of this book, and for the care they have given to the translation.

J. P. S.

London, September 1964

CONTENTS

ACKNOWLEDGMENTS

WE thank the authors and editors who have willingly allowed us to reproduce the following figures and tables:

(*a*) Periodicals:

Acta Crystallographica, Fig. 6.5.

Advances in Energy Conversion, Pergamon Press, Figs. 7.4, 7.5, 7.6, 7.8, 7.9, 7.10 and 7.11.

Annalen der Physik, Fig. 2.6.

Bell System Technical Journal, Fig. 3.2 and 3.6.

Bulletin de la Société Française des Électriciens, Figs. 5.8 and 5.9, Tables 5.1 and 5.2.

Canadian Journal of Physics, National Research Council, Figs. 8.12 and 8.13.

Comptes-Rendus de l'Académie des Sciences, Gauthier-Villars, Figs. 7.2, 7.3, 8.5 and 8.8.

International Journal of Physics and Chemistry of Solids, Pergamon Press, Figs. 4.4, 4.6, 6.6, 8.14 and Tables 6.3 to 6.5.

Journal of Chemical Physics, American Institute of Physics, Fig. 6.3.

Journal of the Chemical Society of London, Fig. 9.2.

Journal of Electronics and Control, Figs. 4.2 and 6.5.

Journal de Physique et le Radium, Société Française de Physique, Figs. 5.12, 5.15, 8.9 and 8.10.

Journal of Polymer Science, Interscience, Figs. 9.9 and 9.10.

Philips Research Reports, Fig. 3.12.

Physica, Fig. 2.14.

Physica Status Solidi, Akademie-Verlag, Figs. 8.1, 8.2, 8.3, 8.4 and 8.15.

Physical Review, American Institute of Physics, Figs. 3.9, 8.11 and 8.18.

Proceedings of the Royal Society of London, Fig. 8.3.

Research, Butterworths Scientific Publications, Fig. 9.6.

Review of Modern Physics, American Institute of Physics, Fig. 2.7.

Transactions of the Faraday Society, Fig. 9.7.

Zeitschrift für Naturforschung, Fig. 6.8.

Zhurnal Tekhnitcheskoe Fiziki, Akademii Nauk USSR, Fig. 4.10.

(*b*) Books:

An Introduction to the Transition-Metal Chemistry (ORGEL), Methuen, London, 1960, Fig. 8.6.

Cours de Cristallographie, I (GAY), Gauthier-Villars, Paris, 1958, Figs. 1.6, 1.7 and 4.8.

The Nature of the Chemical Bond (PAULING), Cornell University Press, Ithaca, 1960, Fig. 6.12.

New Developments in Ferromagnetic Materials (SNOEK), Elsevier, Amsterdam, 1947, Fig. 5.14.

Proceedings of the International Conference on the Physics of Semiconductors, Institute of Physics and The Physical Society, London, Fig. 7.7.

Reports of the Meeting on Semiconductors (Rugby, April 1956), The Physical Society, Figs. 1.15 and 4.1.

Semiconductors (HANNAY), Reinhold, New York, 1959, Figs. 3.3 and 3.7.

Solid State Physics 3 (SEITZ and TURNBULL), Academic Press, New York, 1956, Fig. 3.11.

INTRODUCTION

THIS book develops the text of a conference held at the University of Bordeaux in 1957 under the title 'Défauts de Structure et Semi-conducti-bilité' and reviews recently published work, particularly in the fields of interactions between impurities and the prediction of semiconducting properties.

The mathematical physics aspects, which have been given masterly treatment by P. Aigrain and F. Englert, are not treated here but the references quoted allow the reader to follow them up should he wish. There are also other recently published general works in this field [1, 2, 3, 4, 5, 6, 7, 8].

We try here to present in a readily accessible way certain questions which are of particular interest to chemists, in particular the role played in semi-conductivity by the interatomic bonds in the elementary crystal cell. It is particularly reasonable—as suggested recently by IOFFE and REGEL [9]—that these bonds determine the essential properties of semiconductors.

PRINCIPAL SYMBOLS

c basic co-ordination concentration (Chapter 3)

E_G energy gap

E_1 covalent contribution to E_G

E_2 ionic contribution to E_G

e elementary charge

G Avogadro's number

h Planck's constant

K mass action constant (Chapter 3)

k Boltzmann's constant
rate constant (Chapter 3)
thermal conductivity (Chapter 7)

$\mathbf{k}$ wave number

M symbol for a metal

$\mathcal{M}$ magnetic moment of unit cell

m formal charge

N number of carriers per cm^3

n ionic charge
number of π electrons (Chapter 9)

n   (type or region) conduction by electrons

P number of positive carriers per cm^3

p   (type or region) conduction by holes

q effective charge

r, r' ionic or covalent radii

T symbol for transition element

X symbol for a metalloid

Z, Z' total number of electrons

β_m Bohr magneton

λ_0 atomic ionicity

λ crystalline ionicity

μ electron mobility

η number of valence electrons

ψ, ϕ wavefunction associated with an electron

$[\,]$ iono-covalent partial lattice concentration (Chapter 3)

Chapter 1

ATOMS AND CRYSTALS

1.1 The periodic classification of the elements

WE do not think it necessary to review the basis of the periodic classification of the elements, but it will be useful to keep in mind the scheme for the
different energy levels which may be occupied by electrons around a
nucleus (Fig. 1.1 following PAULING [1.1]), as well as the electronic structures
for the atoms of the principal elements (Table 1.1). We shall distinguish,

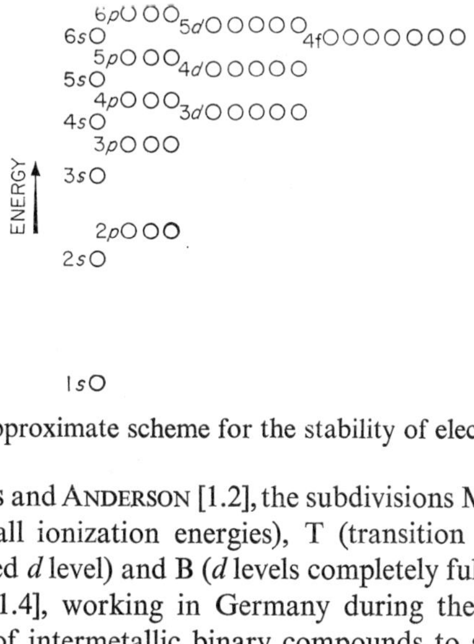

FIG. 1.1. Approximate scheme for the stability of electron levels

following EMELÉUS and ANDERSON [1.2], the subdivisions M (electropositive
metals having small ionization energies), T (transition elements having
a partially occupied d level) and B (d levels completely full). ZINTL and his
colleagues [1.3], [1.4], working in Germany during the 1930's, made a
systematic study of intermetallic binary compounds to see whether they
satisfied Dalton's Law of Definite Proportions according to which the
numerical subscripts attached to the symbols for the elements in chemical
formulae must be integers.

This work showed that the group of elements B (Table 1.1) could be
further subdivided. Combinations MB, TB or BB formed with elements
from the first part of the group (columns I_B to III_B) give rise to series of
compounds, some of which have complicated indices in their chemical

1

TABLE 1.1*

Zintl elements

Levels	Rare gases	I_A	II_A	III_A	IV_A	V_A	VI_A	VII_A	VIII_A	VIII_A	VIII_A	I_B	II_B	III_B	IV_B	V_B	VI_B	VII_B	VIII_B
														B	C	N	O	F	Ne
$2s$	He 0	Li 1	Be 2											2	2	2	2	2	2
$2p$														1	2	3	4	5	6
														Al	Si	P	S	Cl	A
$3s$	Ne 0	Na 1	Mg 2											2	2	2	2	2	2
$3p$														1	2	3	4	5	6
		K	Ca	Sc	Ti	V	Cr	Mn	Fe	Co	Ni	Cu	Zn	Ga	Ge	As	Se	Br	Kr
$3d$	A 0	0	0	1	2	3	5	5	6	7	8	10	10	10	10	10	10	10	10
$4s$	A 0	1	2	2	2	2	1	2	2	2	2	1	2	2	2	2	2	2	2
$4p$														1	2	3	4	5	6
		Rb	Sr	Y	Zr	Cb	Mo	Tc	Ru	Rh	Pd	Ag	Cd	In	Sn	Sb	Te	I	Xe
$4d$	Kr 0	0	0	1	2	4	5	6	7	8	10	10	10	10	10	10	10	10	10
$5s$	Kr 0	1	2	2	2	1	1	1	1	1	0	1	2	2	2	2	2	2	2
$5p$														1	2	3	4	5	6
		Cs	Ba	La	Hf	Ta	W	Re	Os	Ir	Pt	Au	Hg	Tl	Pb	Bi	Po	At	Rn
$4f$	Xe 0	0	0	0	14	14	14	14	14	14	14	14	14	14	14	14	14	14	14
$5d$	Xe 0	0	0	1	2	3	4	5	6	7	9	10	10	10	10	10	10	10	10
$6s$		1	2	2	2	2	2	2	2	2	1	1	2	2	2	2	2	2	2
$6p$														1	2	3	4	5	6
	M			T										B					

* H and 1s level are excluded

formulae. (This is also true of compounds formed between the alkalis and the heavy elements of column IV_B. The subdivision of group B in this region is somewhat indefinite.) Combinations with the remaining elements of group B (columns IV_B to VII_B) give rise to compounds having simple indices, with the exceptions just cited. Table 1.2 lists examples of the compounds formed by magnesium and sodium.

TABLE 1.2

M	M I_B	M II_B	M III_B	M IV_B	M V_B	M VI_B	M VII_B
Mg	Mg_2Cu Mg Cu_2	Mg Zn Mg Zn_2 Mg_2Zn_{11}	Mg_5Ga_2 Mg_2Ga Mg Ga Mg Ga_2	Mg_2Ge	Mg_3As_2	MgSe	$MgBr_2$
Na	Na_2Au Na Au Na Au_2	Na_3Hg Na_5Hg_2 Na_3Hg_2 Na Hg Na_7Hg_8 Na Hg_2 Na Hg_4	Na_6Tl Na_2Tl Na Tl	$Na_{15}Pb_4$ Na_5 Pb_2 Na_2 Pb Na Pb Na Pb_3	Na_3Bi	Na_2Te	NaI

Some of the series of compounds mentioned above obey the rules governing the electron concentration per atom, as is well known for the alloys TB and I_BB, HUME-ROTHERY [1.5]. In agreement with these divisions, we shall give a special character to the subgroup comprising the elements of Columns IV_B to VII_B to the right of the boundary given by Zintl, lying approximately between III_B and IV_B. We shall call these elements the **Zintl elements**.

1.2 Different types of interatomic bonds

In a molecule containing a small number of atoms, or in a giant molecule such as a crystal, the atoms are always bound to one another by means of their electrons. However, the electrons can form bonds in many different ways. Their behaviour depends to a large extent on the **total ionization energy** of the atom; that is to say, the work necessary for the removal of all of the electrons occupying the highest partially-filled level (valence electrons). The result of this operation is a positively-charged ion having the electronic structure of the rare gas preceding the atom in the periodic classification. Table 1.3 gives these energies in electron volts for the principal elements of the groups M and B. The atoms having small total ionization energies (up to about 35 eV) crystallize in the form of arrays of close-packed spheres. A fraction of their valence electrons, freed from the attraction of the nucleus, form an electron gas able to move through the structure under the action of electric fields. This typifies the **metallic bond** and its accompanying 'metallic' electrical conductivity; that is to say, a conductivity which is very large and which diminishes slowly as the temperature is increased. These properties are associated with the elements situated to the left of Table 1.3 and with the 'series' compounds discussed in the preceding section (left-hand groups of Table 1.2).

TABLE 1.3

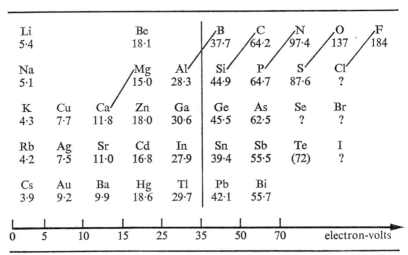

When atoms of small ionization energy bond with atoms of high ionization energy, the latter do not lose their electrons, and on the contrary attempt to complete their valence octet at the expense of the former, i.e. to reach the electronic structure of the rare gas following them in the periodic classification. The subscripts in the chemical formulae for these compounds tend to be simple, single-valued, and determined by the columns of the periodic table to which the constituent atoms belonged (the well-known rules of valency). The arrangements of such atoms in crystals are dictated by considerations of the packing of the different positive and negative ions (**cations** and **anions**) arranged at such a distance that their mutual attraction balances the repulsion between their electron clouds. This is the **ionic bond.** Since all the electrons are retained by the nuclei it is easy to foresee that the electrical conductivity of the chemical compound, when pure and having a perfect crystalline periodicity (thus at very low temperatures), will be zero. This gives a good description of the compounds formed from the atoms situated respectively at the extreme left and extreme right of Table 1.3, with certain reservations now to be discussed.

The picture of rigid spheres which we have given for the ions becomes less precise as the atomic number (and hence the complexity of the atom) increases. FAJANS [1.6] showed that large ions could be deformed by the electric field of their neighbouring ions. The spherical symmetry of the electron cloud around the nucleus is then no longer retained, and an induced dipole is formed, leading to a more or less strong interpenetration of the electron clouds of the different atoms in the directions in which they find their nearest neighbours. The electric field giving rise to this **polarization** is all the more important if it occurs in crystals having small, strongly-charged cations. We shall see later how one can determine the ionic radius, and Table 1.4 gives the ratio of the number of electronic charges carried by the cation to its ionic radius for the principal elements of groups M and B. This ratio gives a rough indication of how far the preceding scheme of ionic bonding will be affected by the formation of dipoles.

For atoms such as B, Ge, Sb, Se, we have already seen that the bonding between identical atoms cannot take place by means of metallic bonds, since the ionization energies are too high (Table 1.3). We see further that the formation of ions such as $Ge^{4+}Ge^{4-}$ or $Se^{6+}Se^{2-}$ will be nullified by their strong polarization. In Table 1.4 these atoms have a ratio greater

TABLE 1.4

					Li 1·67			Be 6·45		B 15·0		C 26·7
	Na 1·05				Mg 3·08		Al 6·00	Si 9·77	P 14·7		S 20·7	Cl 26·9
K 0·75	Cu 1·04	Ca 2·02	Zn 2·70	Ga 4·84	Ge 7·55	As 10·6	Se 14·3	Br 17·9				
Rb 0·68	Ag 0·79	Sr 1·77	Cd 2·06	In 3·70	Sn 5·64	Sb 8·07	Te 10·7	I 14·0				
Cs 0·59	Au 0·73	Ba 1·48	Hg 1·82	Tl 3·16	Pb 4·77	Bi 6·76						

0   0·75   1·3   2·5   5   7   10   15   30

Ratio (elementary charge)/(ionic radius (Å))

than 7, and this completely excludes the formation of ionic bonds. The interpenetration of the electronic clouds takes place along particular privileged directions (tetrahedral configuration for germanium, right-angle spiralled chain for selenium), each atom sharing one of its electrons in common with its neighbour in each of these different directions. An atom cannot acquire by this communal sharing more valence electrons than it possessed at the outset. Only the atoms of Columns IV_B, V_B, VI_B, VII_B in the periodic classification are thus able to complete their octet by forming in this manner either 4, 3, 2 or 1 bond respectively, i.e. as many electron pairs as may be shared per atom. This is the **covalent bond,** whose chief property is its directional character. The electrical conductivity of a crystal bonded in this way, when pure, is zero at low temperature (as for the ionic bond), but increases rapidly as the temperature increases and causes the breaking of a certain number of bonds. This type of conductivity, which differs from metallic conductivity, is called semiconductivity and exists

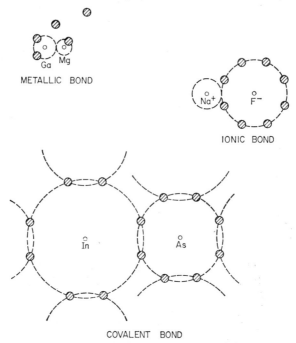

FIG. 1.2. Schemes for different types of interatomic bonds
Electrons are denoted by shaded circles

amongst all non-metallic crystals, although it is particularly important in crystals having covalent or partially covalent bonds. We shall call it **intrinsic** semiconductivity to distinguish it from the other mechanisms causing semiconductivity which will be discussed in Chapter 2.

The combination of Zintl atoms with other atoms by means of a non-metallic bond, can generally be described by a superposition of the characteristics of a purely ionic and purely covalent bond. Figure 1.2 presents the various schemes of interatomic bond described by Lewis and Kossel. The separation for atoms *of comparable mass* increases in passing from metallic bonding to covalent bonding and finally to ionic bonding.

1.3 Orbital wavefunctions and hybridization

There are certain analogies between the motion of a group of electrons and the propagation of a light beam. Louis de Broglie, in the development of a theory of **wave mechanics,** showed that the duality of behaviour, corpuscular (energy, mass, velocity) and wave-like (frequency, wavelength), was present for elementary particles just as much as for electromagnetic radiation (radio-waves, visible light, X-rays, etc.). The wavefunction ψ associated with an electron is a convenient mathematical representation allowing the calculation of the physical properties of a group of electrons by means of the differential equations for a system of waves (cf. [3] and [4]). Just as the energy E of a photon is related by the relation $E = h\nu$ to the frequency ν of the electromagnetic wave carrying the photon, it is the product 'mass $\times$ velocity' of the electron which is connected with the wave number $\mathbf{k} = 1/\lambda$ of the associated wavefunction: $mv = h\mathbf{k}$, when h is Planck's constant,

$$h = 6{\cdot}55 \times 10^{-27} \text{ erg.s} = 4{\cdot}14 \times 10^{-15} \text{ eV.s}$$

(cf. [1]). The wavefunctions of the electrons orbiting around the atomic nuclei are usually called **orbital functions,** and are designated by ψ_s, ψ_p, ψ_d, etc., according to which energy levels are concerned. The quantity $|\psi|^2$ represents the charge density at a point, or the probability of finding an electron at that point. We shall be particularly interested for the moment in the angular distribution of the electrons, which is quite different according to whether we are considering s, p, d or f electrons, etc. Thus for the principal quantum number 2, the orbital functions are the following (cf. [3]);

$$\psi_s = [\tfrac{1}{4}(2\pi a^3)^{\frac{1}{2}}](2 - r/a) \exp(-r/2a)$$
$$\psi_{px} = [\tfrac{1}{4}(2\pi a^3)^{\frac{1}{2}}](r/a) [\exp(-r/2a)] \cos \theta$$
$$\psi_{py} = [\tfrac{1}{4}(2\pi a^3)^{\frac{1}{2}}](r/a) [\exp(-r/2a)] \sin \theta \cos \phi$$
$$\psi_{pz} = [\tfrac{1}{4}(2\pi a^3)^{\frac{1}{2}}](r/a) [\exp(-r/2a)] \sin \theta \sin \phi$$

where r, θ, ϕ, are the polar co-ordinates of a point, origin at the nucleus, and

$$a = h^2/4\pi^2 me^2 = 0{\cdot}529 \text{ Å}$$

is the radius of the first Bohr orbit of the hydrogen atom. Figure 1.3 shows their shape schematically, i.e. spherical for ψ_s, and two spheres touching at the origin and centred on one of the principal axes for ψ_p. It can be shown there are at most for each principal quantum number one ψ_s orbital, 3 ψ_p orbitals at right angles, 5 ψ_d orbitals and 7 ψ_f orbitals. The different orbitals for one of the levels s, p, d or f are equivalent amongst themselves, with different spatial orientations.

Let us consider the diatomic molecule of chlorine, the spiral chain arrangement of hexagonal grey selenium and the double layers observed by RICHTER [1.7] in unstable antimony. We have shown that in each of these three examples the interatomic bond can only be covalent. We have noted in the preceding section that the formation of a complete octet requires 1, 2 or 3 shared electron pairs per atom for the atoms chlorine, selenium and antimony respectively (the electrons in these pairs are shown

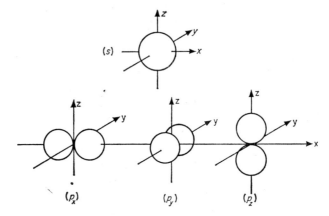

FIG. 1.3. Schematic representation of the angular distribution of electrons in s and p orbitals

by crosses in the diagrams to the left of Fig. 1.4). Table 1.1 shows that these atoms have 1, 2 and 3 unpaired p electrons respectively, and their electronic formulae are developed schematically to the right of Fig. 1.4, where the circles represent the energy levels of the allowed orbitals and the crosses represent the electrons which can occupy them in pairs of opposite spin (in reality each atom only forms a single bond with each of

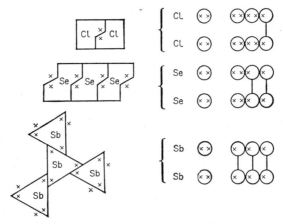

FIG. 1.4. Bonding schemes for unhybridized orbitals

its neighbours). The theoretical considerations developed in the preceding paragraphs allow us to foresee that it must be possible to associate one such orbital function with the two paired electrons shared by the two atoms. These electrons must therefore be unpaired in their respective atoms, and in general belong to such a level as s, p or d. Note that the bond angles formed with p orbitals are virtually always right angles. The

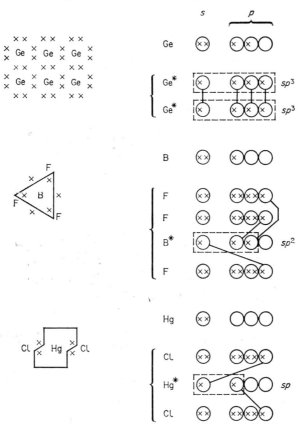

FIG. 1.5. Bonding schemes for hybridized orbitals

arrangements of the atoms will be given more precisely in Section 1.5.

Let us now consider the tetrahedral arrangement of the atoms in germanium (identical to that of the carbon atoms in diamond). The electronic formula of the normal atom only possesses two unpaired p electrons (Fig. 1.5), and we should be tempted to group the atoms like those of selenium. However, the completion of the octet requires four shared pairs of electrons per atom and crystallographic analysis shows that the disposition of the nearest neighbours follows the four rigorously equivalent radii of a tetrahedron. In this case one supposes that there is first an excitation of an electron from an s level to a p level (formula Ge*). Then, following PAULING [1.1], the combination of the wavefunctions ψ_s, ψ_{px}, ψ_{py}, ψ_{pz} gives, with a change of orientation to the axes and considering only the angular distribution, four equivalent wavefunctions called **hybridized orbitals** of the form:

$$s + p_x + p_y + p_z$$
$$s + p_x - p_y - p_z$$
$$s - p_x + p_y - p_z$$
$$s - p_x - p_y + p_z$$

from which one can retrieve the experimental directional maxima and their angles after calculation. This sort of hybridization is written symbolically sp^3, to indicate that we combine one s orbital and three p orbitals. It is obvious that the four bonds between two atoms are shown very schematically and that in reality each atom forms only one bond with each of its neighbours. Figure 1.5 also depicts the case of sp^2 hybrids formed, for example, by the boron atom in the molecule BF_3, and the sp hybrid formed, for example, by the mercury atom in the molecule $HgCl_2$. In the latter two cases the bonds are strongly covalent, they are oriented at 120° in one plane for BF_3 and collinearly for $HgCl_2$. Hybrids of the wavefunctions s, p and d also exist.

The stability of such hybrids formed from atoms excited into higher energy states might seem unusual. In fact it is necessary to distinguish between the electronic energy of the molecule or crystal, the sum of the energies of the electrons of the different constituent atoms, and the electronic energy of these atoms when considered to be isolated and in their ground state. The difference between these energies allows one to arrive at a **bond energy** as a function of the number of bonds formed, and proportional—following PAULING [1.1]—to the overlap of the orbital wavefunctions. One may see that the bond energy will be highest in the case of greatest directivity, and the calculation of the relative magnitudes of these energies for the different types of orbitals allowed gives effectively the following results:

s bonds	1·0	(a priori)
p ,,	1·732	
sp ,,	1·933	
sp^2 ,,	1·991	
sp^3 ,,	2·0	

The greatly increased energy of bonds formed from orbital hybrids allows us to understand their stability, even though their establishment requires a preliminary excitation of the atom (as in the case above), or even if it requires the transfer of electrons between atoms (as we shall see in Chapter 2).

1.4 Crystalline Structure and Ionic Co-ordination

If it were possible to calculate, in a general way, the field of force around each atom, one could forecast in advance the type of bond which these atoms would form between themselves, and the corresponding spatial arrangement to give the smallest potential energy for the crystal. Although so precise a prediction is not possible, one can foresee that atoms having spherically symmetrical fields of force will form dense arrays such as the close-packed or semi-close-packed arrangements of touching spheres. The latter are easily studied from a geometrical standpoint (cf. GAY [1.8], p. 163), allowing us to understand the structure of the elements and of certain metallic compounds, as well as the structure of ionic compounds possessing large anions.

When spheres on a plane are arranged so that they occupy the smallest possible surface area, each sphere will be in contact with six other spheres whose centres A are situated at the corners of a regular hexagon. Such layers are superimposed one upon the other so that they occupy the smallest possible volume, when the projections of the centres of the spheres B belonging to the second plane are equidistant from the centres of three of the spheres belonging to A. The packing coefficient (the number of spheres per unit volume) has a maximum value of 0·74. Each sphere has twelve nearest neighbours equidistant from it, and we say that the co-ordination number, or simply the co-ordination, is 12. Two arrangements are always possible when the third plane of spheres is to be superimposed upon the first two: (a) if the centres of these spheres project through the centres of spheres A in the first plane (Fig. 1.6), the alternation of such planes continues according to the scheme $ABABAB$ and the lattice unit is a regular hexagonal prism; (b) if their centres project at C (Fig. 1.7), the succession of planes follows the scheme $ABCABC$ and one may readily show that the lattice unit is a cube as viewed from one of its corners. The first example is termed the **hexagonal close-packed** array (h.c.p.) and the second, the **face-centred cubic** (f.c.c.). Finally let us mention the existence of an array of pseudo close-packed spheres, **body-centred cubic** (b.c.c.), where the centres of the spheres occupy the corners and the centre of a cube, and for which the packing coefficient is only 0·68. Each of these spheres has eight equidistant nearest neighbours and six neighbours 15% further removed, so that the co-ordination 8 is sometimes considered as a co-ordination 14. The greater part of the metals and a large number of metallic compounds crystallize in one of these three structures.

The spheres considered above do not completely fill the available space

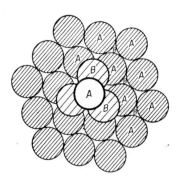

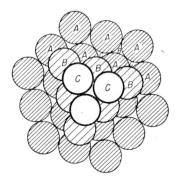

FIG. 1.6. Hexagonal close-packed array of tangential spheres (following GAY [1.8])

FIG. 1.7. Face-centred cubic array of tangential spheres (following GAY [1.8])

and it is of interest to consider the shape and dimensions of the 'cavities' which remain, where other atoms of small dimensions may be located. They are of two sorts, as is shown in Fig. 1.8, i.e. four spheres whose lines of centres are perpendicular form a tetrahedral cavity (t), and two super-imposed groups of three spheres forming an octahedral cavity (o). One can show that close-packed arrays (h.c.p. and f.c.c.) contain 1 (o) and 2 (t) per atom, while the pseudo close-packed array (b.c.c.) contains three (o) for

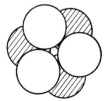

FIG. 1.8. Tetrahedral and octahedral cavities in close-packed arrays

each pair of atoms. In ionic compounds the large anions X^- often take up a close-packed array in the cavities of which the cations M^+ are located. The fraction of occupied cavities will be all the smaller when the charge of the cation is large compared with that of the anion, and as we saw in Section 1.2 such a situation tends towards covalent bonding. A further factor always intervenes; that is, the ratio of the ionic radii r_M/r_X, the calculation and significance of which will be given more precisely in Chapter 6. This ratio determines in effect the **envelopment** of the cations, and purely geo-metrical considerations thus give the maximum possible value of ionic co-ordination. A few of the ionic crystals whose anions X^- form a close-packed array are listed in Table 1.5 in terms of the ratio of their ionic radii r_M/r_X and the co-ordination of their cation. The table considers the simple structures such as those of rocksalt, fluorite, antifluorite (anions

TABLE 1.5

Possible co-ordination		4	6	8	12	Comments
Location of the cation and type of arrangement		Cavities (t) close packed	Cavities (o) close packed	Normal pseudo close packed	Normal close packed	
Ratio r_M/r_X	Cation					
0·154 to 0·224	M^{2+}	BeO h.c.p.				BeO covalent
0·224 to 0·414	M^{3+}		Al_2O_3, NiAs h.c.p.			Covalent character for Al_2O_3, NiAs and MgS (polarization of the anion)
	M^{2+}	ZnS h.c.p.	MgS f.c.c.			
	M^{+}	Li_2S f.c.c.	LiCl, LiBr, LI f.c.c.			
0·414 to 0·732	M^{4+}		TiO_2 h.c.p.			
	M^{3+}		Fe_2O_3 h.c.p.			
	M^{2+}	ZnO, CdS h.c.p.	CdI_2 h.c.p.			
			MgO, CaO, CaS, SrS f.c.c.			
	M^{+}	Li_2O, Na_2O, Na_2S, K_2S f.c.c.	LiF, NaF, NaCl, NaBr, NaI, KBr, KI, RbI, AgCl, AgBr f.c.c.			
greater than 0·732	M^{2+}	O_2Th f.c.c.	SrO, BaO, BaS f.c.c.	CsCl, CsBr, CsI b.c.c.	impossible	
	M^{+}	K_2O, Rb_2O, Rb_2S F_2Ca, F_2Sr f.c.c.	KF, KCl, RbF, RbCl, RbBr, AgF f.c.c.			

f.c.c.), wurtzite, corundum, nickel arsenide, rutile (anions h.c.p.) and caesium chloride (b.c.c.). The case of fluorite is exceptional because the cations (Ca^{2+}, Sr^{2+}, Th^{4+}) form the close-packed array. Hence, a co-ordination of 12 is not allowed in ionic crystal lattices because electro-static neutrality could not be realized.

The case of spinel $MgAl_2O_4$ is worth particular mention. The anions form a close-packed array (f.c.c.) where the cations Al^{3+} are placed in the (o) cavities as in Al_2O_3, while the cations Mg^{2+} are located unusually in the (t) cavities, slightly displacing the anions.

1.5 Covalent Co-ordination and the Phenomenon of Resonance

We now return to the molecules and crystals in which the atoms form directed covalent bonds. Here the co-ordination is fixed completely by the number of electrons used by the atom in orbital bonding functions with the neighbouring atoms. We saw in the preceding section that this number could be forecast from the electronic formulae of the participating atoms. Table 1.6 and Fig. 1.9 give the co-ordination for the principal types of

TABLE 1.6

Orbitals	Co-ordination	Configuration	Example
s	1		Na_2
p	1		Cl_2
p^2	2	Digonal rectangular	Se grey (crystal)
p^3	3	Trigonal pyramidal	Sb unstable (crystal)
sp	2	Digonal linear	Hg in $HgCl_2$
sp^2	3	Trigonal plane	B in BF_3
sp^3	4	Tetrahedral	Ge (crystal)
dsp^2	4	Tetragonal plane	Pt in PtS (crystal)
d^2sp^3	6	Octahedral	Fe in $Fe(CN)_6K_3$ (crystal)

bond including hybrids; their names and corresponding configurations. One should not confuse the trigonal bond (atomic co-ordination 3) and the rhombohedral or trigonal lattice (symmetry axis of order 3) considered in geometrical crystallography. It will be noted that the elements have a co-ordination equal to $(8 - \eta)$, where η is the number of the column in the periodic classification or alternatively the number of valence electrons. This well-known rule, to which we shall return in Chapter 4, shows that the covalent structures are less compact than the ionic structures, since the elements forming non-metallic crystals (on the right in Table 1.4) have large values of η. The double layered atomic structure characteristic of the elements of Column V (As, Sb, Bi) is shown in Fig. 1.10. The bond angles indicated in Figs. 1.9 and 1.10 are the theoretical angles calculated for the hybrid orbital wavefunctions giving the greatest bond energy, and are not always attained in real structures. Thus one finds 106°, 105° and 102° for S, Se and Te, 97°, 96° and 94° for As, Sb and Bi, and we shall see that the angle is often different from 180° for the *sp* hybrid bond.

A study of the different possible spatial arrangements of the valence bonds of an atom has been made by SIDGWICK *et al.* [1.9]. A more general

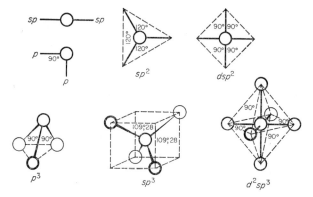

FIG. 1.9. Spatial configurations for different types of bond

study of crystalline structure from the point of view of the co-ordination of the atoms has been recently published by WELLS [1.10]. In order to discuss questions of structure, it is useful to know the symbols of *Strukturbericht*

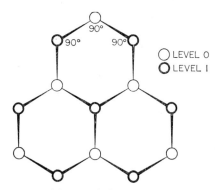

FIG. 1.10. Double atomic layer structure for *p*³ bonds

which are given in Table 1.7 and to which we shall refer in the following chapters. The symbol *A* indicates an element, *B* a compound MX, *C* a compound M₂X or MX₂ and *D* a compound of more complicated formula. This table repeats the ionic structures considered in the preceding sections and includes binary compounds such as ZnS and PbS for

TABLE 1.7

	Arrangement or orbital	Symbol	Element	Symbol	Compound	Symbol	Cavity occupied	Derived compound
Ionic tendency	f.c.c.	A1	Cu			{ C1	(t)	F₂Ca (fluorite) / Li₂O (antifluorite)
						B1	(o)	NaCl (rocksalt)
	b.c.c.	A2	Li	B2	CsCl			
	h.c.p.	A3	Mg			{ B4	(t)	ZnS (wurtzite)
						B8	(o)	NiAs (nickel arsenide)
						C4	(o)	TiO₂ (rutile)
						D5₁	(o)	Al₂O₃ (corundum)
Covalent tendency	sp³	A4	C diamond	B3	ZnS blende	B32	(o)	[CsSb]²⁻Cs₂⁺
	sp/sp³ resonant			C1	Mg₂Sn antifluorite	D0₃	(o)	[Li₂Bi]⁻Li⁺
	p³	A7	As	B29	SnS	C33	(o)	[BiTe₂]⁺S²⁻
	p²	A8	Se					[As]⁻Li⁺
	sp²	A9	C graphite	B12	BN	D0₁₈		[NaAs]Na₂

which the bonding schemes will be explained in the following Chapter (Section 2.5), as well as compounds of the type Mg_2Sn whose partial co-valent character will be better understood when we have discussed the phenomenon of resonance. These are compounds derived from the co-valent lattices, as we shall see in Chapter 3 (compensated lattices).

The concept of a **resonance** between several chemical formulae or modes of bonding has its origin in the mathematical theories of quantum mechan-ics and PAULING [1.1] first presented it in terms readily accessible to the non-expert (cf. [3]). One understands by this phrase that a group of interatomic interactions in a molecule or crystal may sometimes be des-cribed by a combination of simple configurations, none of which have a real existence, but whose formal rapid succession allows the realization of a complex structure somewhat as a rapid succession of stationary images re-constitutes motion. We shall develop this idea when discussing compounds of the family Mg_2Sn which crystallize in the antifluorite structure (Fig. 1.11). Here the co-ordination of the tin atom is equal to 8 (cubic), although

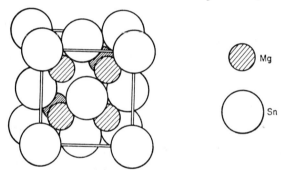

FIG. 1.11. Antifluorite structure (Mg_2Sn)

the properties of this solid force us to consider that the bonds are strongly covalent. Noting that the structure *C1* reverts to the structure *B3* (zinc blende) if we ignore one of the two magnesium atoms, we shall consider the two hypothetical configurations Mg_ISn (Fig. 1.12a) and $Mg_{II}Sn$ (Fig.

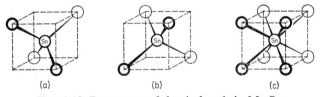

(a)   (b)   (c)

FIG. 1.12. Resonance of the tin bonds in Mg_2Sn

1.12b) which are equivalent except for a symmetry operation, and for which a re-superposition restores the eight nearest neighbours of the tin atom (Fig. 1.12c). We see that we are thus able to reconcile the four directional maxima characteristic of bonds formed from sp^3 orbital hybrids with the co-ordination 8 of atoms of the fourth column in the periodic classification. Because this representation would suggest motion of the assembly if the two partial configurations existed successively, we propose to designate it by the expression **resonance by permutation.**

Now consider the manner of bonding for the magnesium atoms, whose co-ordination is equal to 4 (tetrahedral). We see immediately from Fig. 1.12 that in each configuration (*a* or *b*), one of these atoms is bound to four

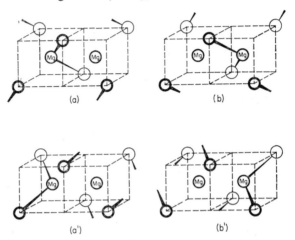

(a)   (b)

(a')   (b')

FIG. 113. Resonance of the magnesium bonds in Mg_2Sn

tin atoms, whilst the other forms no bonds. However, one atom of magnesium possessing only two valence electrons cannot form four bonds. Thus we must consider for these atoms a process of resonance analogous to that for the atoms of tin, i.e. two distinct configurations $Sn_IMg_ISn_{II}$ (Fig. 1.13*a*) and $Sn_{III}Mg_ISn_{IV}$ (Fig. 1.13*a'*) corresponding to that of Fig. 1.12*a* and two others $Sn_IMg_{II}Sn_{II}$ (Fig. 1.13*b*) and $Sn_VMg_{II}Sn_{VI}$ (Fig. 1.13*b'*)

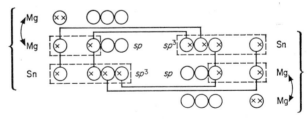

FIG. 1.14. Bonding scheme in Mg_2Sn

corresponding to that of Fig. 1.12*b*. If we attempt to present this in a simplified way by means of a bond scheme similar to that used in Section 1.3, we then obtain Fig. 1.14 where the excited magnesium atom (i.e. the one where an s electron occupies a p level) resonates between two atoms of tin, and where the double arrows indicate for each molecule the possible per-

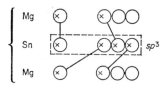

FIG. 1.15. Simplified bonding scheme in Mg_2Sn
(following MOOSER and PEARSON [1.11])

mutation of the formulae s^2 and sp of the magnesium atoms between which the tin atom resonates. If we simplify still more, we arrive at the scheme shown in Fig. 1.15, proposed in 1956 by MOOSER and PEARSON [1.11] without specifying exactly the different resonances considered above.

Chapter 2

PRINCIPAL MECHANISMS OF SEMICONDUCTION

2.1 Defects and Impurities, Rees' Notation

WE are familiar with the regular and periodic arrangement of atoms which characterizes the crystalline state and which is revealed by X-ray analysis. Since Laue's discoveries there has been a tendency to idealize this structure. In fact, crystals always contain defects whose equilibrium concentration is determined by the temperature. One may divide structural defects into two principal categories; those which modify the crystalline regularity at large distances **(dislocations),** and those which have effect only at short distances **(point defects).** A short review of such defects was given recently by FRIEDEL [2.1]. We shall say only little about the former since they do not directly influence the small electrical conductivity of ionic and covalent crystals, but we shall consider the latter at greater length since semi-conductivity is usually due to their presence.

Dislocations are the most usual defects occurring in metallic crystals, which are too compact to allow point defects. The latter—as we shall see—most readily influence the behaviour of other types of crystals. Several recent books have been devoted to the study of dislocations: READ [2.2], COTTRELL [2.3] and FRIEDEL [2.4]. One may classify dislocations in terms of the disturbances that they cause in the direction of greatest atomic density on one or more of the successive lattice planes. The two principal sorts of dislocation are the **edge** or TAYLOR–OROWAN **dislocation** [2.5], [2.6], and the **screw** or **Bürgers dislocation.** The edge dislocation, shown in Fig. 2.1, may be pictured as arising from the insertion of an additional half plane between two infinite crystal planes. The line lying along the edge of this half plane (perpendicular to the plane of the figure, passing through O) is called the dislocation line. Just beyond this line the spacing between two atoms or ions is almost doubled,

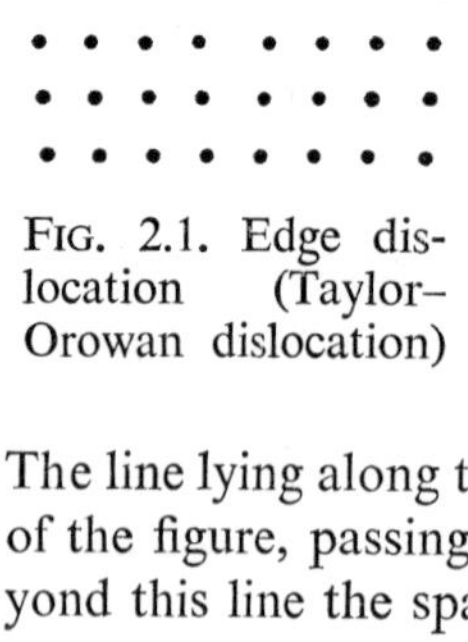

FIG. 2.1. Edge dislocation (Taylor–Orowan dislocation)

but as one moves farther away there is a rapid decrease to the normal spacing. The screw dislocation, illustrated in Fig. 2.2, following FRANK [2.7], plays an important part in the growth of crystals. It consists of a partial shearing of many successive parallel crystal planes following, say, the semi-axis Ox, the direction of shear being perpendicular to these planes and in opposite sense on either side of Ox. This action recalls the *tour de force* of tearing a pack of cards. The line of points where the shearing stops in each plane constitutes the dislocation line. A cylinder having this line as axis (supposed right and perpendicular to Ox) thus cuts the successive lattice planes in a helix whose pitch characterizes this sort of dislocation and is called its **Bürgers Vector.**

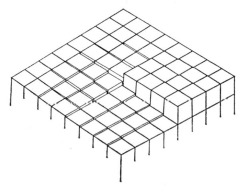

FIG. 2.2. Screw dislocation (Bürgers dislocation)

Amongst the point defects we shall consider successively purely physical structural defects and then impurities or atoms foreign to the chemical formula of the crystal. Physical defects in crystals may be of two different kinds, and there are quite different conditions governing the occurrence of these defects when the temperature—and hence the concentration of defects—increases. Suppose, for the sake of simplicity, that all the atoms of the lattice are identical. In Fig. 2.3a, under the effect of thermal agitation, one atom has passed into an interstitial position. This supposes in general that the neighbouring atoms may be displaced to allow it to pass, and one may suppose that this passage will be all the more difficult when the dimensions of the atom are large and when the crystal packing is most dense. The formation of such a defect, called a **Frenkel defect,** requires an amount of energy W and a probability law of the form $\exp(-W/2kT)$ governs their formation at absolute temperature T (k Boltzmann's constant $= 8 \cdot 62 \times 10^{-5}$ eV/°K). Two defects are created simultaneously: on the one hand an interstitial atom, and on the other a vacancy in the lattice. These may subsequently combine and re-establish the initial state, or they may separate and become independent (Fig. 2.3*b*). In Fig. 2.4*a* (again under the influence of thermal agitation), an atom in the surface of the crystal has passed on to the outside of the initial surface. There are no longer any restrictions imposed by the size of the atom or the nature of the lattice. A vacancy is created which can move into the interior of the

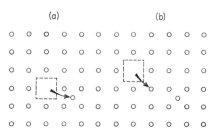

FIG. 2.3. Frenkel defect

crystal (Fig. 2.4*b*). A vacancy will often be created in this way at a dislocation line. This sort of defect is called a **Schottky defect,** and occurs much more readily than a Frenkel defect. The **Tammann temperature,** a temperature equal to half the temperature of melting (expressed in degrees absolute), gives to a good order of magnitude the temperature at which the diffusion of structural defects starts to become appreciable.

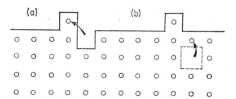

FIG. 2.4. Schottky defect

Finally, in a crystal of specified chemical formula, a foreign atom can diffuse from the outside of the crystal or it may have been incorporated during crystallization from a solution or melt which was chemically impure. This constitutes an **impurity** or chemical defect which may be located interstitially in the lattice or may take the place of one atom of the crystal.

In order to have a clear picture of the distribution of the various kinds of defect in a crystal, it is necessary to develop a logical and coherent notation for defects and **crystallographic sites.** The 'shorthand' notation to be used here to denote the sites is based on that proposed by REES [2.8]: normal sites □ (anion sites ⊟ or cation sites ⊞) and interstitial sites △: electrons will be indicated by e⁻, and gaps in the electron distribution, i.e. **positive holes,** which behave like positive charges with respect to the surrounding electron population, by p⁺. The entity (atom, ion, electron or positive hole) is written, followed by an oblique stroke and the site symbol, the whole being enclosed in brackets. The formation of a mole-fraction x of point defects can be written as follows for the four cases considered above

$$(A/\square) \rightarrow (A_{1-x}/\square)(A_x/\triangle); \text{ Frenkel defect}$$
$$(A/\square_s) \rightarrow (A_{1-x}/\square_s) + xA; \text{ Schottky defect}$$
$$xB + (A/\square) \rightarrow (A/\square)(B_x/\triangle); \text{ interstitial impurity defect}$$
$$xB + (A/\square) \rightarrow (A_{1-x}B_x/\square) + xA; \text{ replacement impurity defect}$$

The subscript s in the second equation denotes a superficial site. The above examples relate to normal sites; other examples below in the text will illustrate further use of the notation. Alternative notations are sometimes used, particularly those of SCHOTTKY (cf. [5]), but will not be dealt with here.

2.2 The Formation and Properties of Colour Centres

We have remarked that physical defects (vacancies and interstitials) occur less frequently in the close-packed arrangements of metallic crystals. Their formation in valence crystals meets with a different sort of obstacle, since it requires the breaking of interatomic bonds without their later re-establishment. The study of these defects is especially interesting in ionic crystals where the electrostatic charges which would result from the non-stoicheiometry, and which would appear locally between anions and cations may be readily compensated by the capture of an electron or of a positive hole in the neighbourhood of the defect. Charged pairs of opposite sign are created abundantly in an illuminated crystal by the photoelectric effect, and their lifetime before recombination is sufficient to allow a local electrically-charged defect to be neutralized very quickly. Large concentrations of vacancies corresponding to only one species of ion are found in non-stoicheiometric crystals.

Figure 2.5a represents an electrically neutral NaCl lattice which is lacking one atom of chlorine. The valence electron of a neighbouring sodium

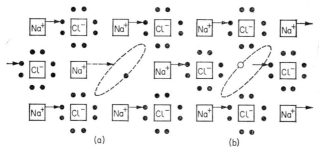

(a)   (b)

FIG. 2.5. F and V_1 colour centres

atom, which would normally be captured by the missing chlorine atom in order to complete its octet, finds itself partially freed and takes up an orbit in the neighbourhood of the defect. Such a combination of anion vacancy and partially-free electron is called an *F* **centre.** If one considers the origin of the defect (for example, a double Schottky defect formed at the surface of the crystal or at a dislocation line, which has migrated to the interior with a separation of the two vacancies), one can note that the absence of the chlorine **ion** Cl^- from the lattice is equivalent to a positive charge, and results in the capture of an electron to re-establish the electrical neutrality of the lattice. *F* centres are created in large numbers in the imperfect lattice of an alkali halide by irradiation with X-rays or ultra-violet light at room temperatures. We write them in Rees' notation:

$$(Cl^-_{1-x}e^-_x/\boxminus)Na^+$$

(Nothing is to be gained by writing Na^+ as $(Na^+/\boxplus)$.)

Figure 2.5*b* represents an electrically neutral sodium chloride lattice which has lost one sodium atom, so that the octet of the neighbouring chlorine atom must be incomplete. In fact, the stability of the octet is such that the atom forms an ion Cl^- by capturing an electron from the normal electronic distribution of the crystal (e.g. a $3p$ electron of sodium). This electron leaves behind it a partially-free positive hole which is able to move from atom to atom in the neighbourhood of the defect. Such a combination of a cationic vacancy and a partially-free hole is known as a V_1 **centre.** If one considers the origin of this defect (i.e. the dissociation of a double vacancy as considered above) one can see that the absence of the **ion** Na^+ from the lattice is equivalent to a negative charge, and entails the capture of a hole in order to re-establish the neutrality of the lattice. V_1 centres are created in large numbers in the imperfect lattice of alkali halides by irradiation with X-rays or ultra-violet radiation at liquid air temperatures. We write in Rees' notation:

$$Cl^-(Na^+_{1-x}\,p^+_x/\boxplus)$$

F and V_1 centres give rise to more or less strong visible coloration of the crystal.

The interpretation of experimental results concerning colour centres has been the subject of many studies since the preliminary work of POHL [2.9], and we shall only cite the relevant work published by SEITZ [2.10], [2.11] from which we take the very brief summary that follows. These considerations are generally applicable to the oxides of the alkaline-earths CaO, SrO and BaO, crystallizing in the *B1* structure. The transition metal oxides, which can display a particular and distinct mechanism for semiconductivity (valence induction) will be considered in Chapter 5.

The electrolytic conductivity which may be observed at high temperatures (in the neighbourhood of the melting point) is almost entirely due to

Schottky defects. The mobility of these vacancies is usually expressed as the frequency of 'jumps', i.e. of displacements of the order of one inter-atomic distance. This frequency is of the order of 10^{-5} s^{-1} for anion vacancies $\boxminus$, of 1 s^{-1} for cation vacancies $\boxplus$, and of 10^4 s^{-1} for vacancy pairs $\boxplus\boxminus$, whose diffusion is therefore of considerable importance (cf. Chapter 3, Section 3.1). The theory of electrolytic transport by such vacancies was given in 1930 by SCHOTTKY and WAGNER [2.12].

F and V_1 centres are antimorphs, and colorations corresponding to very high concentrations (of about 10^{19} cm^{-3}) may be attained with good stability by deliberate use of non-stoicheiometric crystals. The typical shape of the optical absorption bands is shown in Fig. 2.6a, after KLEINSCHROD [2.13] for KCl (F band), and 2.6b, after MOLLWO for KBr (V bands).

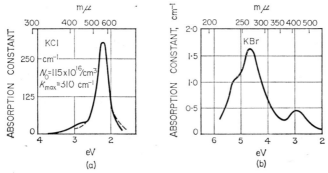

FIG. 2.6. F and V absorption bands

The action of light corresponding to an absorption band leads more or less quickly to a bleaching caused by a grouping into more complex centres known as R or M, from the F centres, or V_2, V_3 and V_4 from the V centres (Fig. 2.7a and b according to SEITZ [2.11]). Moreover, the F centres are susceptible under these conditions to further ionization (F^- centres)

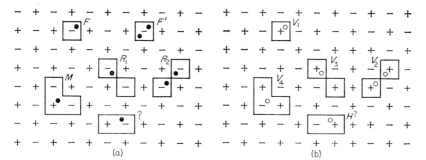

FIG. 2.7. Models of centres derived from F and V_1 centres
(following SEITZ [2.11])

when the temperature is sufficiently low. The V centres are only stable at low temperatures (liquid air), and dissociate rapidly, losing their associated positive holes, when the crystal is warmed to room temperature. The models corresponding to V_2, V_3 and V_4 centres have been discussed by VARLEY [2.14] and SAINT-JAMES [2.15] who have also considered the possibility of halogen atoms in interstitial positions.

These defects may also be created in stoicheiometric crystals by irradiation with X-rays, gamma-rays or beams of charged particles (electrons, protons, etc.), so that in recent years much effort has been put into their study by nuclear physicists. It seems that the effect of such irradiation is particularly complex, involving the intervention of short-lived defects of a new type (excitons), themselves able to create FRENKEL defects [2.14]. Irradiation at low temperatures gives rise to V centres, whilst F centres predominate after irradiation at ambient temperatures. Accidental impurities certainly have an effect, just as internal mechanical strain affects the dislocations which generate the vacancies. The bleaching of irradiated crystals by illumination at wavelengths corresponding to absorption bands can bring into play direct recombination of the loosely bound holes and electrons.

It is found that the electrons or holes bound by a charged vacancy can escape from it and move under the influence of an applied electrostatic field. Measurements have shown that the mobility of the electrons is very small, of the order of 100 cm²/Vs, at liquid air temperature. The measurement of photoconductivity allows one to find their diffusion length.

We have seen in the first chapter that non-metallic crystals are electrical insulators at low temperatures when they are pure and perfect. We have shown here one particular way in which conductivity can arise in **imperfect ionic crystals.** This is the mechanism of **semiconductivity by non-stoicheiometry,** and is characterized by optical transparency in the visible and near u.v. range, by very small carrier mobilities, and by the appearance of electrolytic conductivity at high temperatures. We now continue by considering a further mechanism which gives rise to semiconductivity.

2.3 Properties of Doped Covalent Crystals

In the valence crystals belonging to the fourth column of Mendeleev's periodic table (diamond, silicon, germanium, grey tin), we revert to the example considered in the first section, i.e. to a lattice of completely identical atoms. The communal sharing of the four valence electrons makes up the covalent bonds.

Let us suppose that a foreign atom which is replacing one of the atoms of the lattice can provide only three valence electrons. Figure 2.8 represents an atom of boron in the silicon lattice. It is clear that the boron atom only provides three electrons, whilst the communal sharing system demands four. This indispensable fourth electron will be extracted from the normal electronic distribution of the crystal (being, in the case of silicon, a $3p$ electron) where it will leave a partially-free positive hole able to wander from atom to atom in the neighbourhood of the defect. If the concentration of boron is x atoms per gramme-atom of silicon, the classical formula is then $B_x Si_{1-x}$. Rees' notation has the advantage of specifying precisely that

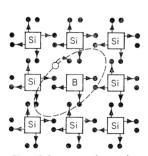

FIG. 2.8. p-type impurity
(tetrahedral bonds)

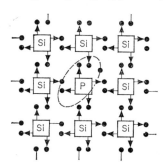

FIG. 2.9. n-type impurity
(tetrahedral bonds)

the boron atoms occupy normal lattice sites, and that a partially-free positive charge is created:

$$(B_x^- \; p_x^+ / \square) Si_{1-x}$$

One may note that the boron atom shown above has the form of an ion B^-, which is natural since all that has happened is that it has accepted an additional electron. The atoms of elements such as boron are called **acceptors** for this reason.

Let us suppose now that the foreign atom replacing one of the atoms of the lattice can provide five valence electrons. Figure 2.9 represents an atom of phosphorus in the silicon lattice. It is clear that the fifth electron cannot be incorporated in the covalent bond; it must find itself partially free, and describes a large orbit round the defect. If the concentration of phosphorus is x atoms per gramme-atom of silicon, the classical formula would be $P_x Si_{1-x}$ and Rees' formula:

$$(P_x^+ \; e_x^- / \square) Si_{1-x}$$

Phosphorus appears here in the form of an ion P^+ since all that has happened is that it has donated an electron. Atoms of elements such as phosphorus are called **donors** for this reason.

One can readily find analogous schemes for the action of impurities having four or six valence electrons in semiconducting arsenic or impurities having five or seven electrons in selenium. An atom of an element from Group V_B may thus be a donor in germanium, inactive in arsenic and an acceptor in selenium. The mechanisms are identical, but those pertaining to germanium and silicon (fourth column of the periodic classification) have been widely known since the invention of the transistor. One may refer in particular to the first chapter of SHOCKLEY's book [2.16] as well as other recent works [5], [7], [8]. The lightly bound electrons or holes orbit about the impurity centres in the same way as those retained by the charged vacancies described in the preceding section, and can be freed under the influence of an electric field. This second mechanism, by which conductivity can arise in **impure covalent crystals,** is called **extrinsic semiconductivity** and is characterized by optical transparency in the infra-red region of the spectrum, and by the high mobility of the carriers. The latter property allows the utilization of junction effects. Because of the importance of such effects (even though their study lies outside the scope of this book) we shall indicate briefly what is meant by mobility, and shall consider, in the following section, the junction effect, which is responsible for the action of rectifiers, photo-voltaic cells, and transistors.

The charge carriers considered above, holes and electrons, each carry the same charge $e = 1.6 \times 10^{-19}$ coulombs, with $+$ or $-$ signs respectively. The resistivity ρ and conductivity σ of the crystal defined by

$$R = \rho \frac{l}{S} = \frac{1}{\sigma} . \frac{l}{S}$$

depend on both N, the number of these carriers per cubic centimetre, and on their average drift velocity μ, called **mobility:**

$$\sigma = N.e.\mu$$

This mobility is the velocity produced by unit applied electric field, and is usually expressed in cm/s for a field of 1 V/cm, or in cm²/Vs. If two types of charge carrier are simultaneously present,

$$\sigma = e(N\mu_n + P\mu_p)$$

where P and N are the numbers of positive and negative charge carriers per cm³ and μ_p and μ_n are the corresponding mobilities. In general, one type of carrier predominates, and one speaks of an n-type or p-type semiconductor. The introduction of an impurity into the crystal is called **doping** (n or p). Mobilities in a single crystal are highest when the crystal is perfect, and the mobilities of electrons are generally greater than those of holes.

One might be tempted to compare a metallic conductor, where the fraction of the free electrons per atom is fixed, with an extrinsic semiconductor, where the fraction of electrons (or holes) is also fixed (at a given temperature) in terms of the concentration of impurities. The essential difference is that electron-hole pairs may be created in a semiconductor, in excess of the existing carriers, by the photoelectric effect or simply by thermal agitation. Such electron-hole pairs recombine very quickly, their lifetime being small (e.g. of the order of one millisecond at most in the case of silicon), except in certain cases which we shall consider in the next section. Thus one may replace the expression for conductivity in an n-type crystal by

$$\sigma = Ne\mu_n + N'e(\mu_n + \mu_p)$$

where N' is the number of unrecombined pairs. It can be seen that the appearance of these pairs increases the conductivity of the crystal. This additional conductivity is called **photoconductivity,** when the pairs are created by the photoelectric effect.

2.4 The Junction Effect and its Practical Importance

If two regions of the same crystal have been doped with impurities which may produce conductivities of oppo-site types, the boundary between these regions possesses interesting properties. Suppose for the moment that these two regions could be arti-ficially separated (this is clearly im-possible without destroying the con-tinuity of the crystalline lattice). We should then have the state represented in Fig. 2.10a, where the circles indi-cate the holes retained by the indium atoms (three valence electrons as for boron) and the black dots represent the electrons retained by the atoms of antimony (five valence electrons as for phosphorus). Returning now to the single crystal (Fig. 2.10b), we see that there has been a superficial neutralization of the electrons and holes on either side of the imaginary boundary and, as a consequence, polarization of this boundary with respect to the more distant neutral crystal. We have on the p-type side the uncompensated negative space charge (indium In⁻), and on the n-type side (antimony Sb⁺) the un-compensated positive space charge. This region which has no charge

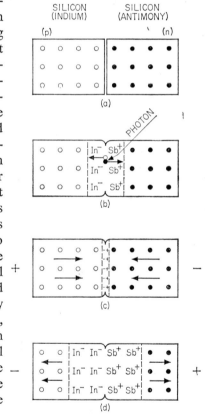

FIG. 2.10. Principles of operation for rectifiers and photovoltaic cells

carriers, but is polarized, is called a **p–n junction.** We see that if a photon creates an electron-hole pair in this region, by the photoelectric effect, these carriers will be separated by the electrostatic field resulting from the polarization; the electron will move toward the n region and the hole toward the p region, although such pairs would recombine rapidly if they were created away from the junction.

Figure 2.10c represents the junction after the application of a potential difference, the p region being made positive and the n region negative. The resulting external electric field is in opposition to the field within the junction and reduces the thickness of the latter, so that the holes from the p region and the electrons from the n region which flow from one part into the other may cross more easily to recombine in either the n or p regions. This picture corresponds to that of a **rectifier** operating in the forward direction. But the figure could equally well represent the unbiased junction illuminated and open-circuited. In this case the photons create carrier pairs which on separating accumulate in the p region (for the holes) and the n region (for the electrons). This results in a positive polarization of the p region and a negative polarization of the n region which oppose the internal polarization of the junction, and the phenomenon stops when an equilibrium is reached. This picture corresponds to that of a **photo-voltaic cell** on open circuit in the limiting case, where the potential difference cannot exceed some particular value because of the leakage current across the small internal resistance of the junction.

Figure 2.10d represents the preceding junction, following the application of an inverse potential difference, the n region being more positive and the p region more negative. The resultant external electric field aids the field within the junction and thickens it, so that the holes from the p region and the electrons from the n region are attracted toward the electrodes leaving behind them a 'no man's land', or more precisely a 'no carrier's land' unfit for all conductivity. This scheme corresponds to that of a rectifier operating in the reverse direction. But the figure could just as well represent the preceding junction after illumination, the two electrodes being joined by a metallic conductor of negligible resistance. In this case the electrons (created as before in the junction) no longer accumulate in the n region. Instead, they give rise to an electric current in the metallic conductor and travel to recombine with the holes at the electrode on the p region. The direction of current in the junction thus corresponds with the polarity indicated. This scheme corresponds to that of a photocell operating under short-circuit conditions, for which the output cannot therefore exceed a value limited by the high internal resistance of the junction.

Let us now consider a crystal in which there are three regions arranged successively in the order p–n–p; potential differences are applied to these regions so that one of the p regions is made positive (the emitter) and the other negative (the collector), whilst the n region in between is kept at an intermediate potential (base). Let us review the behaviour of the two junctions separately for the moment. Figure 2.11a represents the collector to base junction, and the analogy with the scheme shown in Fig. 2.10d shows immediately that this behaves like a rectifier operating in the reverse direction, allowing only a negligible current to flow. Figure 2.11b represents the emitter to base junction, and by analogy with Fig. 2.10c we see immediately that this behaves like a rectifier operating in the forward direction, and passing a substantial current. What happens when we now consider the interaction between the two junctions (Fig. 2.11c)? The electrons and

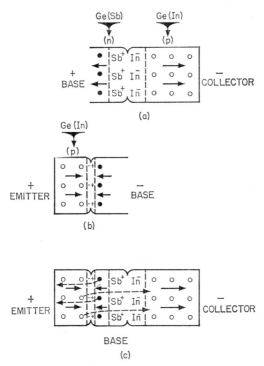

FIG. 2.11. Principles of operation of the transistor

the holes, created in large numbers by the potential difference applied between the emitter and the base, do not all recombine in the p emitter region and n base region, since the internal concentration gradient in the emitter and base carry the electrons which have traversed the p region into emitter, and holes which have traversed the n region toward the collector-base junction. The holes, accelerated by both the internal field of the junction and the applied external field of the same sign, reach the collector as an excess of holes for the p region to which it is joined. In a very approximate way one can say that the transport of charge between collector and base is augmented by an amount corresponding to the emission of the emitter-base junction following the application of a positive potential to the emitter. If we note that the collector-base impedance is very large (that of a rectifier in the reverse direction) and that the emitter-base impedance is on the contrary very small (forward direction of a rectifier), we see that if the current densities crossing them are of the same order, the input and output powers will be very different. Thus we have an arrangement for controlling a large output power (collector-base) by a small input power (emitter-base), in other words, an amplifier. This scheme corresponds to that of a **transistor.**

One sees that the operation of a transistor is related to the lifetime of the minority carriers (holes in the n regions, electrons in the p regions) before their recombination. It is the need to obtain large values of a lifetime which has brought about the technological progress in the purification of germanium and silicon and their crystallization without dislocations. We may note that positive holes play the essential role in the p–n–p transistor. However, in the n–p–n transistor this role, which is important at high frequencies, will be played by the electrons, whose mobilities are much higher. The operation of an n–p–n transistor may be readily deduced from the preceding example.

The junction effect and its applications are theoretically possible in non-stoicheiometric semiconductors, but because of the very small value of carrier mobilities it has not been possible to utilize it here.

2.5 General Case of Inorganic Compounds

The concept of the covalent bond has been defined by Lewis for identical atoms of the elements but its extension to compounds calls for some reservations. On the other hand, the pure ionic bond does not exist, the compound in which it is most closely approached being lithium fluoride. We find in the general case of an inorganic compound MX (where X indicates one of the Zintl atoms) that we require a chemical bond of intermediate character for which at present there is no simple representation or theory. In Section 1.5 we have referred to the idea of resonance, which permits us to replace the direct representation of a group of interatomic interactions by means of a decomposition into two fictitious simple configurations whose superposition reconstitutes the situation studied. The situation here lends itself well to such a procedure and we shall suppose, as was done by SYRKIN and DYATKINA [2.17] for molecules such as HCl, that the wavefunction of a valence electron may be put into the form

$$\psi = C_1 \psi_{\text{cov}} + C_2 \psi_{\text{ion}}$$

This supposes that in considering each compound we could identify the extreme covalent and ionic configurations and the distribution of the electrons in such formulae. The purely ionic bond presents no difficulty since the distribution is fixed by the octet rule. The need to bring the electronic formula of the Zintl atom to that of the rare gas which follows it in the periodic classification gives us formulae such as $Ga^{3+}As^{3-}$, $Zn^{2+}S^{2-}$, $Ag^{+}I^{-}$, $Pb^{2+}S^{2-}$, $Na^{+}Cl^{-}$, etc. . . . However, the case of the co-valent bond is more complicated. We have seen in Section 2.3 that in order to take part in a system of covalent bonds an impurity atom must assume the electronic formula of its host. SHOCKLEY [2.16] and later REES [2.8] have considered the example of an atom of arsenic (As^{+}) taking part in the sp^3 orbital hybrids of crystals of germanium or silicon. PAULING [1.1] on the other hand considered the possibility of providing the chemical symbols with **formal charges** corresponding to the distribution obtained by dividing the shared electron pairs of the linked atoms equally between them, and

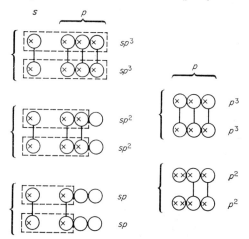

FIG. 2.12. Principal hybridization schemes for covalent bonds

thus wrote, e.g. $R_3N^{+}O^{-}$, trimethylamine oxide. Both modes of reasoning lead to the same notation for the pure covalent bond. Concisely, it may be said that each atom must have in its uppermost level the electronic formula sp^3 in order to form a tetrahedral bond, sp^2 to form a plane trigonal bond, sp to form a digonal linear bond, s^2p^3 or p^3 to form a trigonal pyramidal bond, s^2p^4 or p^4 to form a digonal rectangular bond, etc. . . . as the corresponding bond schemes in Fig. 2.12 demonstrate. Thus we write $Ga^{-}As^{+}$, $Zn^{2-}S^{2+}$, $Ag^{3-}I^{3+}$, $Pb^{-}S^{+}$, $Na^{2-}Cl^{2+}$, etc. . . .

In general such a notation for the extreme covalent configuration pre-supposes the excitation of certain electrons of M or X atoms to higher energy levels (as we saw in Chapter 1, Section 1.3), as well as the transfer of electrons between M and X. When one starts from the electronic formulae of the isolated atoms, such a transfer takes place in the opposite direction to that required for the ionic bond and to which we are accustomed. The energy required for this process as for the excitation of the electrons, must be balanced by the high bond energies of orbital hybrid covalent bonds, and more especially in this case, by the high energies of the intermediate

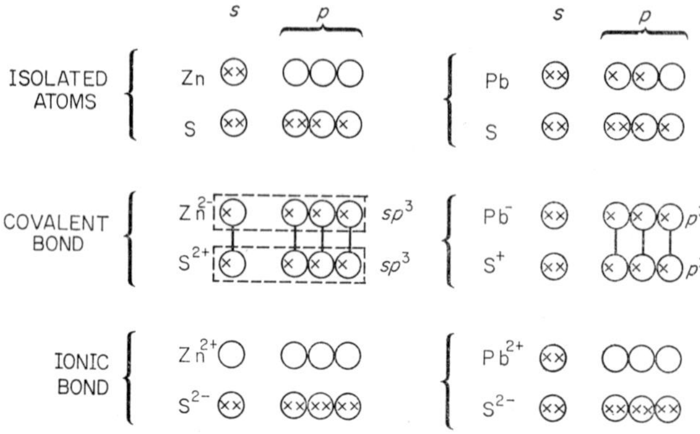

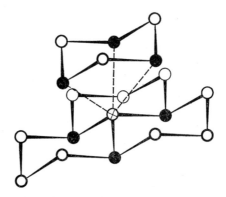

FIG. 2.13. Possible electronic formulae for ZnS and PbS

iono-covalent bonds. Figure 2.13 shows, very schematically, the case of ZnS (zinc blende structure), and of PbS (rocksalt structure). In the latter instance, KREBS [2.18] showed that the octahedral co-ordination arises from the resonance of trigonal pyramidal bonds, of the type exhibited by

FIG. 2.14. Spatial configuration of the resonant trigonal bond
(following KREBS [2.18])

arsenic, between two groups of three atoms arranged in successive double layers. Figure 2.14 is drawn on this basis, and the six atoms involved in the resonant bonds are shown in black. This notation for the pure covalent bond has recently been generalized with a view to predicting semiconductivity in crystal lattices (cf. Chapter 4).

It is essential to note that the charges introduced for the ionic configurations and for the covalent configurations are quite fictitious; they do not allow prediction of the actual sign of the dipole of a bond.

One can gain some idea of the ionic character of a compound by considering, following SUCHET [2.19], that some fraction of the valence electrons is susceptible to be bound to either atom M or to atom X, according to the covalent configuration $M^{m-}X^{m+}$ or ionic configuration $M^{n+}X^{n-}$ considered. This 'nomadic' electron population $c = m + n$ is also equal to the covalent co-ordination, i.e. four for the tetrahedral bonds ($1s + 3p$), three for the trigonal bonds ($1s + 2p$, or $3p$) and two for the digonal bonds ($1s + 1p$, or $2p$) (Fig. 2.15). Each of these c electrons can be represented

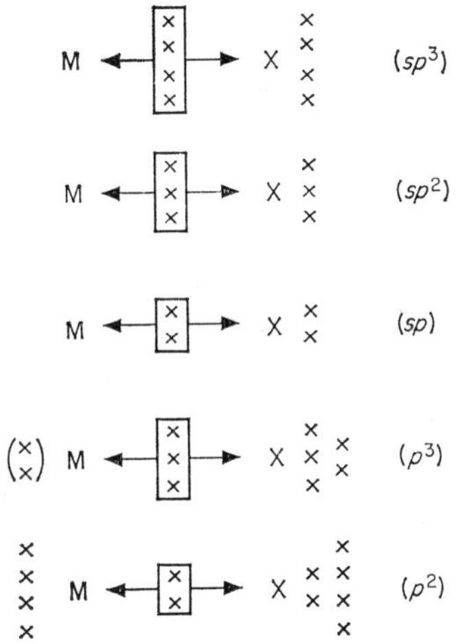

FIG. 2.15. 'Nomadic' and 'Sedentary' electrons in the principal sorts of bond

by a wavefunction ϕ_M about atom M or ϕ_X about atom X. If, as a first approximation, we suppose that these wavefunctions are orthogonal, we can write:

$$\psi_s = a\phi_M + b\phi_X, \quad \text{with } a^2 + b^2 = 1$$

or

$$\psi_s = (1 - \lambda)^{\frac{1}{2}}\phi_M + \lambda^{\frac{1}{2}}\phi_X$$

since the normalization condition requires ψ^2 or ϕ^2 to be equal to unity. Thus the coefficient λ represents the fraction of a nomadic electron bound to X, i.e. in the case of tetrahedral bond, the atom X possesses 4λ (nomadic) + 4 (sedentary) bonding electrons. In a general way the totality of valence electrons taking part in the bond distribute themselves as $c(1 - \lambda)$ on M and $c(1 + \lambda)$ on X.

If we suppose that the molecule MX is formed without change in the electronic formulae of the isolated atoms, the number of bonding electrons possessed by X is known and allows one to calculate a particular value λ_0 of the parameter. Thus for ZnS and the binary II–VI compounds

$$4\lambda_0 + 4 = 6, \quad \text{whence } \lambda_0 = \tfrac{1}{2}$$

Table 2.1 gives the values of λ_0 corresponding to the most important compound semiconductors or their partial lattices, and one can see immediately that these values give a rough evaluation of their ionic character. We call the parameter λ_0 the **atomic ionicity.** However, it is important to note that

TABLE 2.1

Orbital	λ_0	I	II	III	IV	V	VI	VII
sp^2	0				B			
	$\tfrac{1}{3}$			X———————X		(unknown)		
	$\tfrac{2}{3}$	[Na——————————————As]						
				(partial lattice of Na$_3$As)				
sp^3	0				Ge			
	$\tfrac{1}{4}$			In———————Sb				
	$\tfrac{1}{2}$		Zn———————————————————S					
	$\tfrac{3}{4}$	Ag———————————————————————————I						
p^3	0					As		
	$\tfrac{1}{3}$				Pb———————S			
	$\tfrac{2}{3}$			Tl———————————————————I				
p^2	0						Se	
	$\tfrac{1}{2}$			(unknown) X———————X				
p	0							I

the hypothesis made for the diatomic molecule MX (simple juxtaposition of atoms M and X) is quite unacceptable if we now consider a crystal, where a separation of the charges $M^{q+}X^{q-}$ generally intervenes to form a dipole in the sense of the ionic formula. If one takes account of this displacement of electrons, one finds:

$$c(1 + \lambda) = c(1 + \lambda_0) + q,$$

whence
$$\lambda = \lambda_0 + q/c;$$

where q is the **effective charge**; for example for NaCl (p electrons only)

$$3 + 3\lambda = 5 + q, \quad \text{whence } \lambda = \tfrac{2}{3} + q/3$$

We call the parameter λ the **crystalline ionicity.**

Theoretical calculations by SLATER and KOSTER [2.20] for InSb give $q \sim 0$ and $\lambda \sim 0{\cdot}25$. The study of the Raman effect can also give an approximate value for the effective charge, and one thus finds for ZnS, $q \sim 1$ and $\lambda \sim 0.75$ [2.21]. In some cases the diffraction of X-rays also gives an indication, and one has in the case of NaCl, $q \sim 0.8$ and $\lambda \sim 0.9$ [2.22]. Finally, it has been shown recently that experiments on the electron resonance of the free electrons in InSb can give an idea of the effective charge, and the results are compatible with zero charge [2.23]. We shall return to the classical idea of ionicity in Chapter 6. Our concepts, inspired by those of GOODMAN [2.24], for the semi-empirical determination of q and the calculation of λ for any compound whatever will be treated in detail in Chapter 7.

We shall base our arguments on the covalent formulae alone, when we are primarily considering impurity semiconduction and its prediction in new chemical compounds, especially when we have to draw a line between alloys and semiconductors within an intermetallic domain (cf. Chapter 4). On the other hand, we shall base our arguments on the ionic formulae alone, when we are essentially considering semiconduction due to non-stoicheiometry, especially when it is necessary to understand the behaviour of oxide semiconductors (cf. Chapter 5). Finally, we shall take both into consideration and calculate their contribution successively when we wish to determine empirically the electrical characteristics of compounds (cf. Chapters 6 and 7).

Chapter 3

INTERACTIONS BETWEEN DEFECTS; PARTIAL LATTICES

3.1 Diffusion of Defects and Impurities

WE have considered the presence of defects in crystals as an established fact, without concerning ourselves greatly with their origins. Defects often arise by diffusion away from some source (dislocations in the case of physical defects, impure crystal for chemical defects). The laws governing diffusion in solids were formulated by Fick. The first expresses the proportionality existing between the flux J of the diffusing substance (quantity crossing perpendicularly unit surface area of a reference plane during unit time) and the concentration gradient responsible for this flux taken along the axis Ox:

$$J = -D\frac{dc}{dx}$$

The diffusion constant D so defined does not depend upon the concentration c as long as the latter is small (generally the case for semiconductors). It varies rapidly as a function of the absolute temperature following an exponential law

$$D = D_0 \exp(-Q/RT)$$

where Q is the activation energy in calories/mole and R is the gas constant. Table 3.1 gives some values of D for germanium and silicon crystals. Fick's second law gives the variation of the concentration with time:

$$\frac{\partial c}{\partial t} = D\frac{\partial^2 c}{\partial x^2}$$

A number of books and reviews are devoted to the phenomena of diffusion, amongst them: JOST [3.1], LECLAIRE [3.2], SEITH [3.3], SMITS [3.4] and BURCHENALL [3.5]. The particular problems for semiconductors were treated recently—from the technological point of view—by FULLER [3.6] (cf. also REISS and FULLER in [6], p. 222).

TABLE 3.1

Germanium	D (cm²/s) at 850°C	Silicon	D (cm²/s) at 1200°C
Li ⎫ Cu ⎬ Ni ⎭	10^{-5}	Li ⎫ Cu ⎬	10^{-5}
Ag ⎱ Fe ⎰	10^{-6}	Zn ⎫ Fe ⎬ Au ⎭	10^{-6}
Au	10^{-9}		
		{ O	10^{-10} }
P ⎫ Bi		Al	10^{-11}
As ⎬ Sb ⎭	10^{-11}	B ⎫ P ⎬ Ga ⎭	10^{-12}
Ga ⎫ B		Bi ⎫ Sb	
Zn ⎬ In Tl ⎭	10^{-13}	As ⎬ In Tl ⎭	10^{-13}

In a simple and important example shown schematically in Fig. 3.1, the reference plane envisaged above cuts the solid in sections of constant area. The expression for the concentration of the solute in the plane of x axis is then very simple:

$$c = c_0 \text{ erfc } [x/2(Dt)^{\frac{1}{2}}]$$

where the symbol erfc represents (1 — the error function integral, erf)

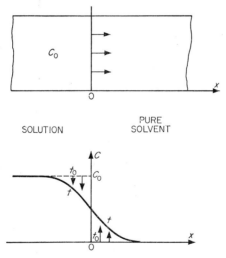

FIG. 3.1. Simple example of diffusion (constant cross-section)

which is a tabulated function. For example, this formula may be applied to the diffusion of an acceptor in a germanium or silicon parallelepiped having a uniform initial donor concentration. One can now calculate the acceptor or donor concentrations N_A or N_D per cm³. The first will be, at a depth x:

$$N_A = N_0 \text{ erfc } [x/2(Dt)^{\frac{1}{2}}]$$

If N_A so defined is greater than N_D, we shall have (N_A-N_D) holes per cm³ (p region), and in the opposite case (N_D-N_A) electrons per cm³ (n region). Thus a p–n junction will be formed at a depth x such that the number of acceptors is equal to that of the donors. If N_0 and N_D are known, then one can produce a junction at a predetermined depth x if one knows the diffusion constant of the acceptor in the crystal used, or equally well determine this value experimentally by measuring x. When N_0 (the number of acceptors initially at the surface) is greater than N_D (the number of donors in the crystal) by several orders of magnitude, one may neglect the latter and use the simplified formula:

$$x = 5\cdot4(Dt)^{\frac{1}{2}}$$

If two impurities diffuse simultaneously one can still usually apply the above formulae, neglecting their interaction (we shall see in the following section that this is only an approximation). We shall consider briefly, as a particular example, the case of the double diffusion of antimony and aluminium in n-type silicon of resistivity 3 ohms-cm, mentioned by TANEN-BAUM and THOMAS [3.7]. The diffusion constants of these two impurities at 1200°C are of the order of 2.10^{-13} and 1.10^{-11} cm²/s respectively, so that the aluminium (an acceptor) will diffuse more deeply than the antimony (a donor) and will form a p region at the front of the diffusion, whilst behind this front the number of donors exceeds that of the acceptors (Fig. 3.2, following the authors cited). If the two metals are deposited on the surface of the silicon by vacuum evaporation, their concentration there is sufficiently high for us to employ the simplified formulae:

$$x_1 = 5\cdot4(2 \times 10^{-13}t)^{\frac{1}{2}} \quad \text{and} \quad x_2 = 5\cdot4(10^{-11}t)^{\frac{1}{2}}$$

Let us suppose that we wish to obtain a very narrow p region of width $x_2 - x_1$, suitable for the high frequency operation of n-p-n transistors, e.g. 2.10^{-4} cm (the value achieved by the authors cited). The diffusion, if carried out at 1200°C, must last just over two minutes, which leads us to consider the use of a much lower temperature in order to have better control over the length of this step in the process.

In ionic crystals, where the diffusion of vacancies consists of a series of jumps from one crystallographic site to the next, the value of the displacement l is nothing more than the constant distance from one atom to its nearest neighbours, and one can show that the diffusion constant can then be written in the form

$$D = \nu l^2/6$$

where ν is the average frequency of the jumps (cf. Chapter 2, Section 2.2). The various formulae given above cannot be applied to the study of the electrolytic conductivity which occurs in these crystals at high temperatures.

Surface effects, whether we are concerned with ionic or covalent crystals, are of particular importance. Fick's first law shows in effect that there will

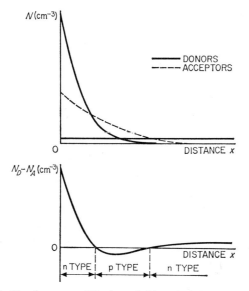

FIG. 3.2. Simultaneous diffusion of Al and Sb in n-type silicon (following TANENBAUM and THOMAS [3.7])

be no diffusion flux in the absence of a concentration gradient. In the case of diffusion into a solid phase from a gaseous phase, this gradient arises from the attachment to the surface of the crystal of a film of solute atoms, often a monatomic film. This phenomenon, called **chemisorption,** involves the establishment of chemical bonds. In other words, the impurity element is attached in such a way as to constitute an extension of the crystal lattice of the host. If one takes the melting temperature T_f of the host (in degrees Kelvin) as a reference, one can assign in a very approximate way a temperature $0.3T_f$ for the onset of chemisorption and $0.5T_f$ (Tammann's temperature) for the onset of diffusion into the interior of the crystal. We shall return to these phenomena in Chapter 5 with reference to the oxides. Chemisorption is of particular importance in catalysis (cf. GERMAIN [3.8]).

3.2 Ion Pairing in Elemental Semiconductors

It may be noted from Table 3.1 that the values of the diffusion constants for germanium and silicon fall neatly into two groups: on the one hand we find those for atoms having small ionization energies, placed at the left of Table 1.3, which is headed by lithium with a diffusion constant of 10^{-5} cm^2/s at the temperatures considered; on the other hand there are those of atoms of high ionization energies; these atoms are situated to the right of Table 1.3, where the logarithm of the diffusion constant is about half that of the first group. Thus it is natural to conclude that the former diffuse via interstitial sites in the form of ions (donor centres such as Li^+e^-) and the latter via normal sites where they take part in the tetrahedral bonds of their host (acceptor centres such as Ga^-p^+ or donors such as P^+e^-). This distinction is confirmed by experiment. The case of an impurity occupying an interstitial site was not considered in Section 2.3 because such an impurity, taking no part in the covalent bond system, would not be included in the first mechanism for semiconductivity which we described. Such a defect written in Rees' notation is identical with that for a Frenkel defect in an ionic crystal, e.g. in the case of zinc oxide which will be treated in Chapter 5 (cf. Fig. 5.1):

$$Ge(Li_x^+ \, e_x^- / \triangle) \quad \text{or} \quad Zn^{2+}(Zn_x^{2+} \, e_{2x}^- / \triangle)O^{2-}$$

If a crystal of germanium or silicon simultaneously contains impurities of both types, then we find in the presence of one another a superposition of the two mechanisms of semiconduction described in the preceding chapter, as shown clearly by writing symbolically:

$$Ge_{1-x}(Ga_x^- \, p_x^+ / \square)(Li_y^+ \, e_y^- / \triangle)$$

It would seem that this superposition of two types of defects creates holes and electrons at the same time, but one can readily foresee that recombination will intervene. In fact, both theory and experiment agree in fixing at each temperature the number of charge carriers/cm^3 for a given crystal, and Fig. 3.3, following [6], shows the logarithmic variation as a function of $1/T$ for germanium and silicon. We saw in Section 1.2 that a pure and perfect non-metallic crystal at very low temperatures was an insulator, but that when the temperature was increased, a few electrons N_i were freed by thermal agitation and left behind in the electron clouds of the atoms an equal number N_i of holes. This weak electrical conductivity is called the **intrinsic** conductivity of the crystal, whilst the increased conductivity resulting from doping with impurities is called **extrinsic**. The numbers N and P of electrons and holes in crystals in electrical equilibrium usually obey the fundamental relationship:

$$N.P = N_i^2.$$

We see that the electrons bound to the lithium and the holes bound to the gallium will recombine and we shall write the formula for the crystal, if for example $x > y$:

$$\text{Ge}_{1-x}(\text{Ga}_x^-\ \text{p}_{x-y}^+/\square)(\text{Li}_y^+/\triangle)$$

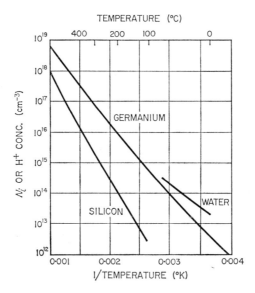

FIG. 3.3. Number of intrinsic carriers at various temperatures (following HANNAY [6])

The analogy between the equation $NP = N_i^2$, the equation expressing the dissociation of water into ions H^+ and OH^-

$$[H^+][OH^-] = N^2 \quad (10^{-14} \text{ at room temperature})$$

and the possibility of applying the laws of mass action and chemical kinetics (concerning these laws see for example SIMON and GERMAIN [3.9]) to the 'solutions' of defects in crystals has been apparent for a long time to workers trying to account qualitatively for phenomena in the non-stoicheiometric oxides. For example, for zinc oxide subject to a variable partial pressure of oxygen BAUMBACH and WAGNER [3.10] wrote the equation shown in Fig. 3.4. The application of the analogy with aqueous

$$2\text{ZnO} \rightleftharpoons 2\text{Zn} + \text{O}_2$$
$$\Updownarrow$$
$$2\text{Zn}^+ \rightleftharpoons 2\text{Zn}^{2+} + 2\text{e}^-$$
$$+$$
$$2\text{e}^-$$

FIG. 3.4. Dissociation of zinc oxide

solutions to the interaction between interstitial and substitutional impurities in valence crystals has been developed in a very important publication by REISS, FULLER and MORIN [3.11] who have shown experimentally the

$$Li(Sn) \rightleftharpoons Li(Si) \rightleftharpoons Li^+ + e^-$$
$$+$$
$$B(Si) \rightleftharpoons B^- + p^+$$
$$\updownarrow$$
$$(e^-p^+)$$

FIG. 3.5. Electron-hole equilibrium in silicon doped with B + Li

existence of interactions, such as those represented in Fig. 3.5 for a silicon crystal containing boron and lithium simultaneously. Symbolically (e^-p^+) indicates a recombined electron-hole pair.

Let us suppose that N_D represents the number of lithium donors/cm³ and $N_{Li\ ext}$ and $N_{Li\ sol}$ the numbers of lithium atoms/cm³ in the tin alloy (external phase) and in the silicon (in solution, not ionized) respectively, and N the number of free electrons/cm³. Applying the mass action law to the two successive equilibria gives:

$$K_1 = N_{Li\ sol}/N_{Li\ ext},$$
$$K_2 = N_D.N/N_{Li\ sol},$$

whence
$$N_D.N = N_{Li\ ext}.K_1.K_2 = K_3,$$

since the concentration in the tin alloy is constant (0·18% of lithium by weight in the experiments cited). It is clear that any increase in the number N of free electrons per cm³ will reduce the ionization, and as a consequence the solubility of the lithium, since its atoms are practically all ionized. Thus we must expect the presence of substitutional impurities (donor or acceptor centres) to affect the solubility of the lithium. This is well confirmed by the experiments cited, illustrated by Fig. 3.6, showing the solubility of lithium as a function of the number N_A of boron atoms per cm³. These curves obey the equation:

$$N_D = N_A/(1 + B) + [N_A^2/(1 + B)^2 + (N_D^0)^2]^{\frac{1}{2}}$$

where
$$B = [1 + (2N_i/N_D^0)^2]^{\frac{1}{2}}$$

derived by REISS and FULLER [3.12] with the help of the preceding considerations, where N_D^0 represents the solubility of lithium in pure silicon.

One can go still further and suggest the existence of an electrostatic attraction between the fixed negatively-charged acceptors and the positively-charged mobile lithium ions, with a new application of the mass action law for the formation of such **ion pairs**:

$$K_P = N_P/N_A.N_D$$

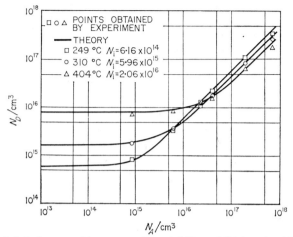

FIG. 3.6. Influence of boron on the solubility of lithium in silicon
(following REISS and FULLER [3.11])

and the calculations of BAUMBACH and WAGNER [3.12] give the equations:

$$K_3 = (N_D^0)^2/2 + [(N_D^0)^4/4 + N_i^2(N_D^0)^2]^{\frac{1}{2}}$$
$$(1 + N_i^2/K_3)N_D = K_3/N_D + N_D/(1 + K_P N_D)$$
$$N_P = K_P N_A/(1 + K_P N_D)$$

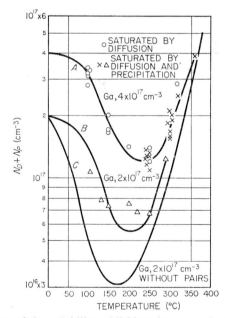

FIG. 3.7. Variation of the solubility of lithium in germanium as a function of
temperature (following HANNAY [6])

allowing the successive calculation of the constant K_3, the number N_D of lithium donor atoms and N_P the number of lithium atoms forming pairs. These relationships have been verified by experiments on the solubility of lithium in germanium doped with gallium. Figure 3.7 shows the good agreement found between experiment and the theoretical curve drawn from the above equations, whilst one is led to very small values of the solubility by neglecting the existence of pairs. The minima result from the more rapid increase of the term B than of the term N_D^0 with increasing temperature. The interactions shown in Fig. 3.5 will now be written according to Fig. 3.8, taking into consideration the ion pairs (B^-Li^+). The existence of ion triplets $(Zn^{2-}Li^+{}_2)$ has also been demonstrated.

$$
\begin{array}{ccc}
Li(Sn) \rightleftharpoons Li^+ & + & e^- \\
+ & & + \\
B^- & & p^+ \\
\Updownarrow & & \Updownarrow \\
(Li^+B^-) & & (e^-p^+)
\end{array}
$$

FIG. 3.8. Formation and equilibrium for atomic pairs Li^+B^-.

3.3 The Case of Oxygen in Silicon

We shall treat in some detail the case of oxygen in silicon, which provides an excellent illustration of the procedure applicable to the study of the behaviour of impurities in covalent crystals. This example is of great practical importance elsewhere, since the exact understanding of the influence of oxygen has led to the frequent adoption of the floating zone process for the preparation of silicon crystals under vacuum.

Many research workers studied this problem between 1954 and 1958 and accumulated various observations, the most important of which will now be enumerated. The quantity of donors present in the crystal appears to be considerably augmented by re-heating for several hours at some temperature between 400 and 500°C, then diminishes and stabilizes if the operation is carried on. These supplementary donors disappear after re-heating to a temperature greater than 500°C. Their presence is related to the oxygen content, of the order of 10^{18} atoms per cm^3, found in crystals pulled from silicon melted in a quartz (SiO_2) crucible. The intensity of the optical absorption band at 9 microns gives a method of measuring the concentration of the oxygen. One finds that the initial rate of formation of these donors at a given temperature is proportional to the fourth power of this concentration, $[O]^4$. Because the solubility of the oxygen decreases with decreasing temperature, the crystals are supersaturated and a prolonged annealing brings about in time the precipitation of silica as a second phase. The Tyndal effect following from this is clearly observable in the infra-red following an annealing at 1000°C which has thereby a stabilizing effect on the crystals.

After having reconsidered and analysed all these earlier results KAISER, FRISCH and REISS [3.13] proposed in 1958 a theory taking account of the known facts. This theory supposes that the oxygen atoms dissolve in the crystal during the course of thermal treatment and accumulate at particular privileged points in the form of atomic aggregates of successive composition $[SiO_2]$, $[SiO_3]$, $[SiO_4]$, $[SiO_4SiO]$ ..., $(SiO_2)_n$. The first aggregates would behave as donors, but would become electrically inactive when they had acquired a certain number of oxygen atoms and would end by precipitating in the form of a second phase when this number had become very large. The kinetics of the various aggregation reactions are much simplified if one supposes that only atomic oxygen is mobile, the other aggregates being fixed, and that the majority of the inverse reactions (dispersion of the aggregates) may be neglected. The ith reaction by which the aggregate A_i attaches a new oxygen atom, can be written to a first approximation:

$$A_i + O \longrightarrow A_{i+1}$$

and the mass action laws and chemical kinetics:

$$K_i = [A_{i+1}]/[A_i][O]$$
$$d[A_{i+1}]/dt = k_i[A_i][O]$$

and we may suppose that the oxygen concentration varies little and takes for [O] the initial concentration in the crystal.

We can now note that from the second to the fourth oxygen atom the steric factor is increasing, and foresee that the first and second reactions will approach their pseudo-equilibrium more quickly than the third reaction. At a certain temperature, such as 450°C, the number of aggregates A_4 will thus be able to grow at the expense of that of the aggregates A_2 and A_3 if the coefficient k_4 is not too large. The application of the kinetic law to reactions 3 and 4 gives:

$$d[A_4]/dt = k_3[O][A_3] - k_4[O][A_4]$$

where, by supposing that 1 and 2 have reached equilibrium:

$$d[A_4]/dt = k_3 K_1 K_2[O]^4 - k_4[O][A_4]$$

which brings us to consider, at time t in the neighbourhood of t_0, the fictitious reaction $4O \rightarrow A_4$ having coefficient $k = k_3 K_1 K_2$. The expression so obtained

$$d[A_4]/dt = k[O]^4 - k_4[O][A_4]$$

accounts well for the proportionality with $[O]^4$ found experimentally for the initial rate of formation of the donors, and for the existence of a maximum concentration of donors, on the condition that the latter are essentially made up of aggregate A_4, i.e. (SiO_4), the aggregates A_5 and higher being inactive. The value of this maximum is equal to $(k/k_4)[O]^3$ and, before it has been reached, the donor concentration is approximately:

$$[A_4] = [A_4]_{max}[1 - \exp(ct)]$$

Comparison with the experimental results gives, in CGS units: $k = 1 \cdot 2 \cdot 10^{60}$ and, at 450°C, $k/k_4 = 5 \cdot 10^{-38}$ and $c = 1 \cdot 8 \cdot 10^{-5}$. The authors cited have developed a complete theory, more precise than the approximation above, and their calculations are in good agreement with experiment. We reproduce in Fig. 3.9 the variations that this theory predicts as a function of

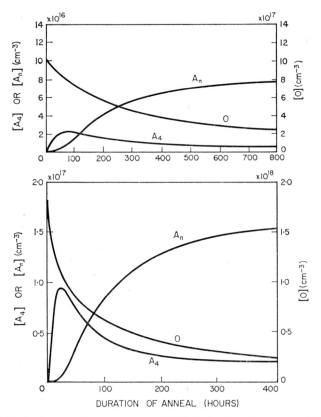

FIG. 3.9. Evolution of aggregates at 450°C (following KAISER et al. [3.13])

time for the concentration of aggregates A_4 (donors) and A_n (inactive) in crystals of silicon initially containing 10^{18} and $1 \cdot 8 \cdot 10^{18}$ oxygen atoms per cm³ during annealing at 450°C. Concentrations less than 10^{18} do not give a maximum for A_4.

Two points in the above call for remark. The first is that there is an uncertainty about the crystallographic sites occupied by the oxygen atoms before annealing. The relatively large value of the diffusion constant (of the order of 10^{-18} cm²/s at 450°C) leads one to presume that they are interstitial sites. On this point one may note that the radius of neutral oxygen is 0·66 Å, being of the same order of magnitude as the ionic radius of Li⁺ (0·60 Å). The second point is that real crystals generally contain impurities other than oxygen; hence the probable formation of atomic pairs which will modify the mechanisms set out, but may also assist in their elucidation. SUCHET [3.14] has reviewed the publications in this field; he considers that the oxygen atoms diffuse via interstitial sites by inserting themselves momentarily into the Si–Si bonds according to the scheme of

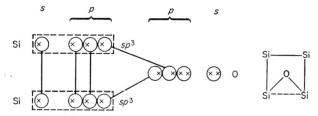

FIG. 3.10. Si–O–Si bonds before annealing

Fig. 3.10; moreover, as a result of the partially ionic character of the Si–O bond, they carry an effective negative charge. Taking into account the information furnished by the existence of entities such as:

$$Si_{1-2x}(Al_x^- O_x^{2+} e_x^- /\square) \quad \text{and} \quad Si(Li_x^+ O_x\, e_x/\triangle)$$

he suggested that the presence of [SiO₄] donor centres in the theory of KAISER et al. [3.12] could be represented by a formula such as:

$$Si_{1-x}(O_x^+\, e_x^-/\square)(O_{3x}/\triangle)$$

The presence of an oxygen atom in a substitutional position is stabilized by the effective negative charge shared amongst the three interstitial atoms.

3.4 Interactions Between Defects in Compound Semiconductors

In compounds the interactions between defects assume a much more complex character than in the elements. The intermediate character of the interatomic bonds here brings into play both mechanisms for semiconductivity described in the preceding chapter. We shall have to consider on the one hand the lattice of normal crystallographic sites, able to take up substitutional impurities as well as anion and cation vacancies (Schottky defects), and on the other hand the lattice of interstitial crystallographic sites, able to take up interstitial impurities as well as the anions and cations displaced from the normal lattice (Frenkel defects). In general, we shall be able, without inconvenience, to utilize ionic charges for the interstitial lattice, but we shall have to employ formal and ionic charges simultaneously for the normal lattice, taking into account whenever possible the magnitude of the effective charge.

A simple case, which immediately extends the interactions set out in Section 3.2, is that of the binary III–V compounds such as AlSb and GaSb, which always exhibit a spontaneous stoicheiometric defect (antimony vacancies causing a p-type conductivity of the order of 10^{17} carriers per cm³). KOVER and QUILLIET [3.15], and later HROSTOWSKI and FULLER [3.16], showed the possibility of obtaining a partial compensation by the addition of lithium before (doping the melt) or after (diffusion) crystallization. This result may be interpreted by using either a covalent formula or an ionic formula:

cov. $\quad \text{Al}^-(\text{Sb}^+_{1-x}\,\text{p}^+_x/\square) + y\text{Li} \rightarrow \text{Al}^-(\text{Sb}^+_{1-x}\,\text{p}^+_{x-y}/\square)(\text{Li}^+_y/\triangle)$

ion. $\quad \text{Sb}^{3-}(\text{Al}^{3+}_{1-x}\,\text{p}^+_{3x}/\boxplus) + y\text{Li} \rightarrow \text{Sb}^{3-}(\text{Al}^{3+}_{1-x}\,\text{p}^+_{3x-y}/\boxplus)(\text{Li}^+_y/\triangle)$

The fact that these compounds are known to decompose slightly at the melting temperature because of the high vapour pressure of antimony (Schottky defects) allows a choice to be made between the two representations and permits the conclusion that the sign of the dipole is expressed by $\text{Al}^{(-)}\text{Sb}^{(+)}$, which is in conformity with the covalent formula and hence with a negative effective charge. The ionicity parameter defined in Section 2.5 is thus smaller in value than $\lambda_0 = 0.25$. Let us finally remark that the lithium has been shown in the interstitial sites where it diffuses, but that in all probability it is located at the site of a vacancy without being integrated into the bonding system.

We now go on to consider the case of compounds where the ionic structure predominates, for which KRÖGER and VINK [3.17] have published a very complete study in 1956 (cf. also THOMAS in [6], p. 269). In dealing with this we shall introduce certain simplifications into the notation for defects:

Cation vacancies $\quad(-/\boxplus)\quad$ written $\boxplus^-$
$\qquad\qquad\qquad\quad(\text{p}^+/\boxplus)\qquad\qquad\quad\boxplus$

Anion vacancies $\quad(-/\boxminus)\quad$ written $\boxminus^+$
$\qquad\qquad\qquad(\text{e}^-/\boxminus)\qquad\qquad\quad\boxminus$

Interstitial cations $(\text{M}/\triangle)\quad$ written $\triangle$
$\qquad\qquad\qquad\quad(\text{M}^+/\triangle)\qquad\qquad\quad\triangle^+$

The simplest case that one could imagine is that of the compound MX in equilibrium at high temperature with the vapour of M which we shall assume to be monatomic. For simplicity one supposes that only the cation sub-lattice may have defects (vacancies and interstitials). If the temperature is high enough, one may consider that the defects are ionized. The equilibrium with the vapour having partial pressure P_M, the Frenkel equilibrium, the intrinsic equilibrium of electrons and holes and the neutrality condition for the crystal then give us four equations permitting the determination of the four unknown equilibrium constants:

$$N\,[\triangle^+] = K_1 P_M \qquad (1)$$
$$[\triangle^+][\boxplus^-] = K_2 \qquad (2)$$
$$N.P = N_i^2 = K_3 \qquad (3)$$
$$N + [\boxplus^-] = P + [\triangle^+] \qquad (4)$$

An approximate method of graphical solution has been proposed by BROUWER [3.18] by writing the equations in logarithmic form. This necessitates a little simplification of the fourth equation by considering three distinct regions: for small values of P_M the concentration of interstitial cations is neglected ($[\boxplus^-] = P$); for large values the concentration of cation vacancies is neglected ($[\triangle^+] = N$), and for the intermediate region one neglects the type of defect whose equilibrium constant is the smallest according to whether one has $K_2 < K_3$ ($N = P$) or $K_2 > K_3$ ($[\boxplus^-] = [\triangle^+]$). Figure 3.11 illustrates the second case. The sharp angles shown in this

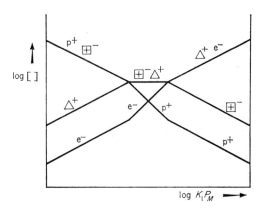

FIG. 3.11. High temperature equilibrium between MX and the vapour of M (following KRÖGER and VINK [3.17])

figure must naturally be smoothed off. The logarithms of the four unknown quantities, such as are set out in Table 3.2, are in effect linear functions of $\log K_1 P_M$ having slopes 0·5 and 1·0. The width of the intermediate region is equal to $\log (K_2/K_3)$.

Another approximation concerns a compound MX in equilibrium at a high temperature with the vapours M (monatomic) and X_2 (diatomic) and

TABLE 3.2

	Low P_M	Intermediate region	High P_M
$\log N =$	$0 \cdot 5 \log (K_3/K_2)$ $+ 0 \cdot 5 \log K_1 P_M$	$-0 \cdot 5 \log K_2$ $+ \log K_1 P_M$	$0 \cdot 5 \log K_1 P_M$
$\log P =$	$0 \cdot 5 \log K_2 K_3$ $- 0 \cdot 5 \log K_1 P_M$	$0 \cdot 5 \log K_2 K_3^2$ $- \log K_1 P_M$	$\log K_3$ $- 0 \cdot 5 \log K_1 P_M$
$\log [\triangle^+] =$	$0 \cdot 5 \log (K_2/K_3)$ $+ 0 \cdot 5 \log K_1 P_M$	$0 \cdot 5 \log K_2$	$0 \cdot 5 \log K_1 P_M$
$\log [\boxplus^-] =$	$0 \cdot 5 \log K_2 K_3$ $- 0 \cdot 5 \log K_1 P_M$	$0 \cdot 5 \log K_2$	$\log K_2$ $- 0 \cdot 5 \log K_1 P_M$

the vacancies $\boxplus$ and $\boxminus$, without any interstitials. Thus one has the five relationships:

$$N[\boxminus^+] = K_1 P_M \qquad (1)$$
$$P[\boxplus^-] = K_1' P_x^{\frac{1}{2}} \qquad (1')$$
$$[\boxplus^-][\boxminus^+] = K_2 \qquad (2)$$
$$N.P = K_3 \qquad (3)$$
$$N + [\boxplus^-] = P + [\boxminus^+] \qquad (4)$$

which may be solved by analogous considerations. This model has been applied to the interpretation of the results obtained on CdS by KRÖGER *et al.* [3.19] and on PbS by BLOEM [3.20]. During these experiments, the partial pressure of sulphur was controlled by means of an auxiliary furnace heating a piece of sulphur at the extremity of the enclosure, whilst the principal furnace heated the compound at the other extremity to a much higher temperature. One finds in the first case $K_2 \simeq 10^{33}$, $K_3 \simeq 2.10^{32}$ at 900°C, and in the second $K_2 \simeq 4.10^{34}$, $K_3 \simeq 10^{36}$ at 1000°C.

More complicated models are necessary if foreign atoms are incorporated in the lattice, e.g. Ga in CdS (donor) and Bi (donor) or Ag (acceptor) in PbS. The intrinsic point, for which $P = N$, is thus displaced toward higher sulphur pressures (in the case of donors) or lower pressures (in the case of acceptors). Figure 3.12, following Bloem, illustrates the high temperature equilibrium for PbS doped with 2.10^{18} atoms per cm^3 of bismuth, which may be written in Rees' notation (region 3) by supposing that the value of the effective charge is $0 \cdot 6$ e (cf. Chapter 7).

$$\text{cov.} \quad Pb_{1-x}^-(Bi_x \, e_x^- / \square)S^+$$
$$\text{ion.} \quad Pb_{1-x}^{2+}(Bi_x^{3+} \, e_x^- / \boxplus)S^{2-}$$
$$\text{actual} \quad Pb_{1-x}^{0 \cdot 6+}(Bi_x^{1 \cdot 6+} \, e_x^- / \boxplus)S^{0 \cdot 6-}$$

where, for example, in the presence of lead vacancies

$$\text{cov.} \quad Pb^-_{1-x-y}(Bi_x\ e^-_{x+y}/\square)S^+$$

$$\text{ion.} \quad Pb^{2+}_{1-x-y}(Bi^{3+}_x\ e^-_{x-2y}/\boxplus)S^{2-}$$

$$\text{actual} \quad Pb^{0\cdot6+}_{1-x-y}(Bi^{1\cdot6+}_x\ e^-_{x-0\cdot6y}/\boxplus)S^{0\cdot6-}$$

or in the presence of Pb vacancies and Cu^+ interstitials (not considered in the figure):

$$\text{cov.} \quad Pb^-_{1-x-y}(Bi_x\ e^-_{x+y+z}/\square)S^+(Cu^+_z/\triangle)$$

$$\text{ion.} \quad Pb^{2+}_{1-x-y}(Bi^{3+}_x\ e^-_{x-2y+z}/\boxplus)S^{2-}(Cu^+_z/\triangle)$$

$$\text{actual} \quad Pb^{0\cdot6+}_{1-x-y}(Bi^{1\cdot6+}_x\ e^-_{x-0\cdot6y+z}/\boxplus)S^{0\cdot6-}(Cu^+_z/\triangle)$$

3.5 Partial Lattices and Compensated Lattices

At the beginning of the preceding section we noted that it was convenient to consider the following two lattices as distinct: (*a*) the lattice of normal crystallographic sites, with iono-covalent interatomic bonds and with effective charges intermediate between the formal charges and the ionic charges; and (*b*) the lattice of interstitial crystallographic sites, devoid of interatomic bonds and with pure ionic charges. We may apply this distinction to a crystal of germanium doped with gallium in which lithium has been diffused so as to exactly compensate the p-type conductivity:

$$Ge_{1-x}(Ga^-_x/\square)(Li^+_x/\triangle)$$

It is possible to revert to a classical notation which still retains the concept of separate lattices if we write in brackets those atoms between which iono-covalent bonds exist:

$$[Ge_{1-x}Ga^-_x]Li^+_x \quad \text{or} \quad [Ge_{1-x}Ga_x]^{x-}Li^{x+}$$

The solubilities of gallium and lithium in germanium are very small; otherwise we might imagine that for $x = 1$ we would obtain a compound $[GeGa]^-Li^+$ where the first lattice, of the type *B3* (blende), contains alternately atoms of germanium and of gallium, whilst the lithium atoms occupy the interstitial sites. This is the notation extolled elsewhere by KETELAAR [3] for the 'onium' compounds such as $[NH_4]^+Cl^-$ or $[BF_4]^-H^+$, where there are iono-covalent bonds between the atoms of the molecular groups NH_4^+ and BF_4^-.

SUCHET [3.21] proposed to treat atomic arrangements, such as $[GeGa]^-$ as iono-covalent **partial lattices** and to apply to them the same arguments as to other compound semiconductors. The crystalline ensemble is thus a **compensated lattice** where the ions in the interstitial sites have no other role to play than to assure the electrical neutrality of the crystal by means of electron transfers, so that one may speak of them as a **compensating**

interstitial lattice (CIL). It is found that the partial lattices such as [GeGa]⁻ or [GeAs]⁺, deriving like SiC from the elements of Group IV (with tetrahedral bonds) do not exist, the blende structure apparently not suiting itself to such an arrangement. On the other hand, deriving from the elements of Group V which have pyramidal trigonal bonds (double layers of the arsenic type), we find the partial lattice [BiTe]⁺ in a variety of compounds having the *C33* structure. An example is tetradymite Bi_2Te_2S or $[BiTe]_2^+S^{2-}$, which is analogous to the imaginary compound $[GeAs]^+I^-$. Figure 3.13 illustrates this idea, which is partially justified by the known existence of a phase BiTe in the bismuth-tellurium phase diagram.

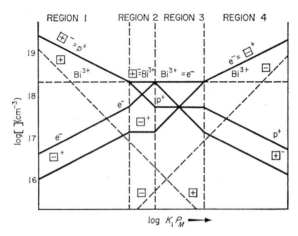

Fig. 3.12. High temperature equilibrium of PbS (Bi) with its vapours (following Bloem [3.20])

The value of the above idea will be best understood by its application to bismuth-telluride Bi_2Te_3, which crystallizes in the same structure as tetradymite and which has been the subject of much work because of the large values of thermo-electric power which it exhibits (400 $\mu V/°C$ between suitably doped n and p-type crystals). The crystal structure reveals a succession of clusters of five atomic layers in the order Te_a-Bi-Te_b-Bi-Te_a, so that its ionic formula would be:

$$Bi_2^{3+}(Te^{2-}/\boxminus_a)_2(Te^{2-}/\boxminus_b)$$

On the other hand, it is readily shown that covalent bonds would not be able to unite all the atoms without the intervention of d^2sp^3 orbital hybrids for the atoms Te_b [3.22]. The simplest covalent formula is then:

partial lattice—(CIL)

$$(BiTe^+/\square)_2(Te^{2-}/\triangle)$$

When this compound is prepared by the fusion of the pure elements in stoicheiometric proportions (account taken of the loss of tellurium inherent in this technique), it is always obtained with a p-type conductivity, and a large excess of tellurium in the lattice, of the order of $0\cdot1\%$, is necessary

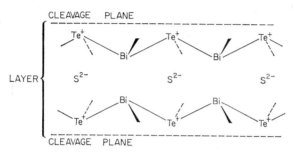

FIG. 3.13. Compensated lattice for tetradymite, Bi_2Te_2S

to obtain n-type material [3.23]. A simple explanation of this anomaly lies in the supposition that there is a poor distribution of the tellurium atoms between the two sorts of crystallographic site, on the condition that the charges they support there are of different sign, i.e. conforming with the formal charges of the covalent formula:

$$\text{stoich.:} (BiTe^+_{1-x} p^+_{3x}/\square)_2(Te^{2-}_{1+2x}/\triangle)$$

$$+ 4x \text{ Te}: (Bi_{1-x}Te^+_{1+x} p^+_x/\square)_2(Te^{2-}_{1+2x}/\triangle)$$

$$+ 8x \text{ Te}: (Bi_{1-3x}Te^+_{1+3x} e^-_x/\square)_2(Te^{2-}_{1+2x}/\triangle) \text{ etc.} \ldots$$

Too great an excess of tellurium naturally leads to the formation of a second phase. The normal behaviour of lithium is to create donor centres (as in germanium and silicon). However, at concentrations of the order of $0\cdot01\%$ it increases the acceptor nature of the compound [3.24]. This effect may be explained by the stabilizing influence of the lithium on the excess tellurium in the CIL. The Li^+ ions are at first located in this compensating lattice before passing, at higher concentrations, into the partial lattice $[BiTe]^+$. When one passes from $[BiTe]^+_2 Te^{2-}$ to $[BiTe]^+_2 Se^{2-}$, the energy of the Bi–Te bond within the brackets increases. This is not shown by a noticeable decrease of the interatomic distance [3.25] because of the perturbing influence of the interstitial ions (Se^{2-} polarizes the bismuth atom), but is amply proved by the increase from $0\cdot15$ to $0\cdot30$ eV of the energy gap (cf. Chapter 6), [3.26]. From this fact, the atoms of selenium, unlike those of tellurium, probably tend to be located in substitutional sites, giving rise to an n-type conductivity:

$$\text{stoich.:} (BiTe^+Se^+_x e^-_{3x}/\square)_2(Se^{2-}_{1-2x}/\triangle)$$

The systematic study and discussion of the nature of the interatomic bonds in the I–V compounds reveals the existence of a few compensated lattices distributed between various different structures [3.27]. The presence of two different crystallographic sites for the lithium atoms in the compounds α Li_3Sb and Li_3Bi crystallizing in the DO_3 structure has been known for a long time, and KREBS [3.28] suggested that one of the atoms, in the form Li^+, does not participate in the bonds, whilst the remaining atoms form a lattice $[Li_2Sb]^-$ or $[Li_2Bi]$ of the $C1$ type (antifluorite). In the compound Cs_3Sb, crystallizing in the $B32$ structure (NaTl), one may show that only one of the caesium atoms participates with the antimony in tetrahedral bonds of the $B3$ type (blende), the others forming a CIL of Cs^+ ions. The DO_{18} structure of sodium arsenide Na_3As is shown to be composed of a partial lattice [NaAs] having the $B12$ structure of boron nitride and of interstitial 'molecules', Na_2. The compounds LiAs and NaSb may be written finally $[As]^-Li^+$ and $[Sb]^-Na^+$, the elementary partial lattices having a chain structure analogous to the $A8$ structure of selenium and tellurium. It is these various compensated lattices which we have included in Table 1.7, as derived compounds of simple structure with covalent tendency.

The compensated lattices are likely to present simultaneously the characteristic features of both mechanisms of semiconductivity defined in Chapter 2. Thus, in the plane of the partial lattice, crystals of Bi_2Te_3 possess the high electronic mobility which characterizes crystals of a preponderantly covalent formula (800 cm²/Vs). However, this value is considerably smaller in the perpendicular direction where the bonds between the CIL and the partial lattice are essentially ionic. In Cs_3Sb, MIYAZAWA et al. [3.29] have demonstrated the appearance of electrolytic conductivity typical of ionic crystals at high temperatures with the deposition Cs^+ ions at the cathode, whilst the electron mobility arising from the partial lattice is, nevertheless, 500 cm²/Vs at room temperature.

Finally, let us note that in Chapter 9 we shall meet organic compensated lattices where the partial lattice [R] is an aromatic hydrocarbon or a related cyclic compound.

Chapter 4

CONDITIONS FOR THE EXISTENCE
OF A COVALENT BOND SCHEME*

4.1 Mooser and Pearson's Rule and its Origins

THE nature of the bonds in different semiconductors has been studied by
KREBS and SCHOTTKY [4.2] and later KREBS [4.3], [4.4], [4.5]. It appears that
certain covalent characteristics can usually be recognized amongst them.
MOOSER and PEARSON [4.6] proposed a simple empirical rule for the prediction of the semiconducting character of a compound from knowledge
of its stoicheiometric formula and the valencies of its component atoms.
Their idea is based on the following postulates:

(1) A connexion between the intrinsic semiconductivity of the solid and
    the essentially covalent nature of the bonds between its atoms exists
    because the difference of electronegativity Δx between the con-
    stituents is generally less than unity. According to Pauling this cor-
    responds to an ionic character of not more than 25%.
(2) Whilst covalent bonds between identical atoms require that the s and
    p electron levels must be completely filled, in compounds this condi-
    tion is only retained for the most electronegative atom, the other
    atoms not forming bonds amongst themselves.

This rule may then be written:

$$n_e/n_a + b = 8$$

where n_e is the total number of valence electrons corresponding to the
stoicheiometric formula, n_a the number of atoms belonging to Groups IV
to VII (excluding the transition metals) and b the number of bonds which
these latter atoms form amongst themselves. The privileged position of
atoms from Groups IV–VII is readily explained by noting that an atom
cannot gain a number of electrons greater than its valency in the process
of sharing in common electron pairs, and that only an atom already possessing at least four valence electrons can complete its s and p levels, to the

* The covalent formulae are used systematically in this chapter. Cf. ref. [4.1].

full octet. Table 4.1 reproduces the examples given by these authors for the application of their rule.

Mooser and Pearson [4.7], [4.8] developed their ideas by considering

TABLE 4.1

Substance	Δ_x	n_e	n_a	b
Ge	0	4	1	4
As	0	5	1	3
Se	0	6	1	2
CdSb	0·3	7	1	1
InSb	0·5	8	1	0
CdTe	0·6	8	1	0
Mg_2Sn	0·6	8	1	0
Mg_3Sb_2	0·6	16	2	0
SiC	0·7	8	2	4
AgI	0·8	8	1	0
In_2Te_3	0·8	24	3	0
Li_3Bi	0·8	8	1	0
$AgInTe_2$		16	2	0
$BaTiO_3$		24	3	0

successively various structures and discussed the particular examples from the work of Krebs which supported them. By considering the *B3* structure of zinc blende as a close-packed array of S atoms, the Zn atoms occupying half of the tetrahedral cavities, the *C1* structure of Mg_2Sn is deduced from it by considering the complete occupation of the tetrahedral cavities by Mg atoms. In the DO_3 structure of Li_3Bi the three Li atoms occupy the octahedral cavities (cf. Table 1.7). The phenomenon of pivotal resonance was invoked for Mg_2Sn (cf. Section 1.5 and Fig. 1.15) and it had already been suggested that for Li_3Bi the lithium atoms in the octahedral sites did not participate in the bonds [4.5] [cf. Section 3.5]. The ortho-rhombic structure of CdSb and ZnSb is treated as a deformed *B3* structure and an Sb–Sb bond is considered to exist (Fig. 4.1). The tetragonal structure of TlSe contains two different crystallographic sites for the thallium atoms, half of which do not partici-pate in covalent bonds (Fig. 4.2).

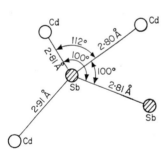

Fig. 4.1. Angles and bond lengths in CdSb (following Mooser and Pearson [4.6])

We shall now attempt to understand the origin of this rule. We saw in the first chapter that the work of Zintl suggested a special behaviour for the elements belonging to Columns IV–VII of the periodic classification, and in this rule we find again the intervention of these same 'Zintl atoms'. Metallurgists are quite familiar with the '$8 - \eta$' rule attributed to Bradley and Hume-Rothery, according to which each atom has $8 - \eta$ nearest neighbours, η being the number of the column of the periodic classification to which the element belongs. It simply expresses the fact that these atoms

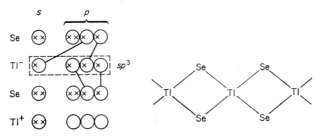

FIG. 4.2. Bond scheme in TlSe (following MOOSER and PEARSON [4.7])

tend to complete their outer shell by the formation of covalent bonds, and hence they acquire as many supplementary electrons as they form bonds (cf. Section 1.2). If $a = \eta$ is the number of valence electrons ($s + p$) of the atom and $b = 8 - \eta$ the number of bonds which it forms with its neighbours, that is to say—only in the case of an element—the covalent co-ordination, one can write:

$$a + b = 8$$

If we now suppose, following Mooser and Pearson, that the semiconductivity related to the existence of a continuous covalent lattice can subsist even though the lattice is no longer formed from identical atoms, we see that semiconducting compounds will be formed for those compounds having a simple formula MB or BB cited in Section 1.1, and that a rule for the electronic concentration per atom, analogous to the Hume-Rothery rules [4.9], can be deduced from the equation above by replacing a by the number of valence electrons per Zintl atom n_e/n_a. Thus we return to Mooser and Pearson's rule where the semiconducting compound is considered simply as an element 'inflated' by a dowry of foreign electrons. In fact, such a rule only expresses the conditions for the existence of a covalent bonding scheme.

4.2 Review and Extension of this Rule

MOOSER and PEARSON had the great merit of recognizing the existence of chemical criteria common to all the semiconducting compounds, the inadequate nature of mathematical theories for their investigation, and of extracting from the work of KREBS and SCHOTTKY [4.2] a simple and often effective rule. However, serious criticism may be raised against their ideas, based on the important exceptions to this rule such as the groups of compounds of which we cite representative examples below, together with, in brackets, the number obtained from the expression $n_e/n_a + b$:

Blende structure: Cu_2SnTe_3, (6)
Chalcopyrite structure: $CdSnAs_2$, (5, 3)
Famatinite structure: Cu_3SbS_4, (6, 4)
Antifluorite structure: Li_5GeP_3, (6)
Rocksalt structure: PbS, (5)
Wolfsbergite structure: $TlSbS_2$, (6, 6)
Other structures: PbI_2, (6); Bi_2Te_3, (5, 6); TlSe, (9); GaS, (9); etc. . . .

In the first place the two postulates upon which these authors base their arguments are open to discussion. There is no completely covalent bond between different atoms, any more than there is a purely ionic bond. We must only consider an **iono-covalent** bond for which the ionic character, which Pauling based on the notion of electronegativity alone, is not suitable for the description of semiconducting compounds (cf. Section 2.5). The importance of the covalent component of the interatomic bonds does not arise simply with an ionic character of less than 25%—it exists just as much for NaCl ($\lambda = 0.9$) as for InSb ($\lambda = 0.25$)—but from the fact that it is one constituent characteristic of the iono-covalent bond. It distinguishes it from the metallic bond where some fraction of the valence electrons always forms a free particle gas. If one classifies compounds according to their increasing ionic character—intermetallic alloys (Na_2Cs, Cu_3Al), intermetallic semiconductors (InSb, HgTe), oxides and sulphides (ZnS, MgO), alkali halides (NaCl)—one demonstrates that this covalent characteristic provides the transition between the metallic bond and the ionic features of the iono-covalent bond. There is no possible confusion between an alkali halide and a metallic alloy, so that all attempts at the prediction of semiconductivity reduce to establishing within an intermetallic regime a means of discrimination between those crystal lattices where a covalent character is possible and those where it is not.

Secondly, the expression of the rule lacks clarity, both in the definition of n_e as well as in the value of the number which appears as the right-hand term. In the preceding section we showed that this rule could be deduced from the condition $a + b = 8$ between the total number a of valence electrons for the atoms ($s + p$), and b the number of bonds formed by each atom; this is the condition for the existence of a simple lattice of covalent character. But this condition and the relation that it expresses is only rigorously valid for a bond formed by s-p orbital hybrids, since we have implicitly supposed—in giving them both an identical role—that the electrons occupying the s and p levels cannot be distinguished, just as in the case of sp^3 bonding orbitals which also have 8 electrons. If one wishes to generalize this rule, it is necessary to define a as the number of valence electrons capable of participating in bonding orbitals (s and p electrons for orbital hybrids, but p electrons only for pure p orbitals) and carry over to the right-hand term the total number $2c$ of electrons occupying the different levels in a covalent scheme (8 for the sp^3 octet, 6 for the sp^2 or p^3 sextet, etc. . . ., cf. Section 2.5). Thus one finds that the arithmetic relationships $a + b = 6$ and $a + b = 4$ apply to trigonal pyramidal (p^3) and digonal rectangular (p^2) bonds respectively. In conclusion, n_e *must be defined as the number of valence electrons able to participate in covalent bonds compatible with the crystalline structure* (total number ($s + p$) for the *B3* blende structure and related structures, for the *C1* fluorite structure and for the *B12* structure of boron nitride, (p) only for the *B29* structure of tin sulphide and for the *B1* structure of rocksalt). The figure appearing as the right-hand term must be 8 for cubic and tetrahedral bonds, and 6 for trigonal and octahedral bonds.

Finally, the definition of n_a is imprecise for ternary and quaternary compounds because there one finds, as we shall see in the following section, Zintl atoms occupying different crystallographic sites in the normal lattice. The structure of ternary and quaternary compounds are often in effect the same as those of the binary compounds, or derive from them in a simple way. Thus one can show a correspondence between a first category of sites—the 'cation sites' for the binary compound—and a second category—the 'anion sites' (Zintl atoms). Experience shows that Mooser and Pearson's rule for the tetrahedral bond and the analogous rules for other types of bond can only be employed if the atoms occupying the sites in the first category (placed between parentheses) are not reckoned in n_a. Table 4.2 sets out again most of the exceptions cited above and shows how the rule may be applied to them. The case of Bi_2Te_3 has been examined in Section 3.5 and we saw that there was reason to consider the partial lattice

TABLE 4.2

Compound	Structure	Orbital	Electrons counted in n_e	n_e	n_a	$n_e/n_a + b$
$(Cu_2Sn)Te_3$	Blende	sp^3	s and p	24	3	8
$(CdSn)As_2$	Chalcopyrite	sp^3	s and p	16	2	8
$(Cu_3Sb)S_4$	Famatinite	sp^3	s and p	32	4	8
$(Li_5Ge)P_3$	Antifluorite	sp^3	s and p	24	3	8
PbS	Rocksalt	p^3	p	6	1	6
$(TlSb)S_2$	Wolfsbergite	p^3	p	12	2	6
PbI_2		p^3	p	12	2	6
$[BiTe]^+$		p^3	p	7–1	2	6

[BiTe]$^+$ where $b = 3$ (b is zero for all the other compounds in Table 4.2) and where the charge [ ]$^+$ represents one electron deducted from the total.

It should always be noted that, *in the absence of p electrons,* s electrons can be excited into p levels to take part in p orbital bonds. Thus one finds with the rocksalt structure, besides PbS, the group CaS, SrS, BaS, BaSe, etc. . . . and also the alkali halides. In the wolfsbergite structure, NaSbS$_2$ and CuSbS$_2$ accompany TlSbS$_2$ and the compounds PbI$_2$ and CdI$_2$ crystallize in the same structure.

4.3 Covalent Notation and Rules of Filiation

We have just noted the interest in comparing various compounds which have related structures and bonds which use the same sort of orbital; the different atoms distributed in the anion or cation sites derive one from the other as we pass from one compound to the other. Thus in the series of analogous structures blende–chalcopyrite–stannite cited by WELLS [4.10]

$$\text{ZnS–(CuFe)S}_2\text{–(Cu}_2\text{FeSn)S}_4$$

it is clear that the groups of atoms CuSe and Cu$_2$FeSn are substituted for the zinc atoms in the cation sites. In order that Mooser and Pearson's rule shall continue to be verified in spite of these substitutions, it is necessary and sufficient that these groups be iso-electronic, that is to say that the average number of valence electrons of the substituent shall be equal to that for zinc. This condition can easily be visualized by using the formal charges and the pure covalent notation which we discussed in Section 2.5. Thus one obtains

$$\text{Zn}_4^{2-}\text{S}_4^{2+} - (\text{Cu}_2^{3-}\text{Fe}_2^-)\text{S}_4^{2+} - (\text{Cu}_2^{3-}\text{Fe}^{2-}\text{Sn})\text{S}_4^{2+}$$

which displays very clearly, within the brackets, the conservation of the total number of electrons participating in the bonds, i.e. four per atom in the case of the sp^3 bond. If each column of the periodic classification is represented by its number in roman numerals, the formal charges of the different elements for the various sorts of bonding orbital will be as follows:

$$sp^3: \quad \text{I}^{3-}\ \text{II}^{2-}\ \text{III}^{1-}\ \text{IV}^0\ \ \text{V}^{1+}\ \text{VI}^{2+}\ \text{VII}^{3+}$$
$$sp^2: \quad \text{I}^{2-}\ \text{II}^{1-}\ \text{III}^0\ \ \text{IV}^{1+}\ \text{V}^{2+}\ \text{VI}^{3+}\ \text{VII}^{4+}$$
$$sp: \quad \text{I}^{1-}\ \text{II}^0\ \ \text{III}^{1+}\ \text{IV}^{2+}\ \text{V}^{3+}\ \text{VI}^{4+}\ \text{VII}^{5+}$$
$$p^3: \quad (\text{I}^{2-}\ \text{II}^{1-})\ \text{III}^{2-}\ \text{IV}^{1-}\ \text{V}^0\ \ \text{VI}^{1+}\ \text{VII}^{2+}$$
$$p^2: \qquad\qquad\quad \text{III}^{3-}\ \text{IV}^{2-}\ \text{V}^{1-}\ \text{VI}^0\ \ \text{VII}^{1+}$$

The case of s electrons excited into p states is indicated in brackets. Thus one can write the blende–chalcopyrite–stannite relationship symbolically as follows:

$$\text{II}_4^{2-}\ \text{VI}_4^{2+} - (\text{I}_2^{3-}\ \text{III}_2^-)\text{VI}_4^{2+} - (\text{I}_2^{3-}\ \text{II}^{2-}\ \text{IV})\text{VI}_4^{2+}$$

The interest of such notation is that it allows the prediction of a large number of possible compound semiconductors, which automatically obey rules of the type proposed by Mooser and Pearson, thus making their application unnecessary. Experiments have demonstrated the usefulness of such a method, and, if certain of the compounds foreseen do not exist, it is usually possible to understand the reason for this in terms of the sizes of the different atoms.

We shall now try to compile an inventory of possible atomic arrangements and the various compounds by means of which such **rules of filiation** may be formulated. If the two sorts of atoms constituting a binary compound use the same type of bonding orbital, they are evidently related to the elemental semiconductors, on either side of which they are symmetrically disposed in the periodic classification. Thus the binary compounds $III^- V^+$, $II^{2-} VI^{2+}$ and $I^{3-} VII^{3+}$ are related to the elements of Column IV of the classification with the same tetrahedral (sp^3) or cubic (sp^3 resonant) bond, the binary $IV^- VI^+$ (possibly $II^- VI^+$) and $III^{2-} VII^{2+}$ compounds (possibly $I^{2-} VII^{2+}$) are similarly related to the elements of Column V in the periodic classification and have the same trigonal pyramidal (p^9) or octahedral (p^3 resonant) bond; the binary $II^- IV^+$ (unknown) and $I^{2-} V^{2+}$ compounds could be derived from a hypothetical form of boron with the $A9$, (sp^2) bonds. If the two atoms do not make use of the same type of bonding orbital, they constitute an original arrangement. Examples are: the binary $II_2 IV$ and $I_2^- VI^{2+}$ compounds with sp/sp^3 resonant bonds, the binary II V, and $I^- VI^+$ compounds with sp/p^3 bonds, the binary $IV VI_2$ and $II^{2-} VII_2^+$ compounds with sp^3/p^2 bonds, and the binary IV V and $III^- VI^+$ compounds with sp^3/p^3 bonds. We shall return to these examples in the following section in order to include them in our rules of filiation.

A few remarks must be made apropos of these different arrangements. The first concerns the distinction between elements of Groups I_A, II_A and I_B, II_B, the former having their underlying d level empty and the latter having it full (cf. Fig. 1.1). It appears that the I_A and II_A atoms enter into combination and form resonant bonds more readily than they form normal bonds. Thus one passes from the sp^3 bond of the *B3* (blende) structure of AgI to the *B2* structure of CsCl; that is to say the co-ordination is doubled by a resonance by permutation between 8 neighbours instead of 4. Similarly in the case of the p^3 bond one passes from the *B29* structure of SnS to the *B1* structure of CaS and BaS. Finally the sp/sp^3 resonant bond is found almost uniquely in compounds of the I_A or II_A atoms (antifluorite *C1*). Thus it seems that the presence of the ten electrons in the underlying d level partially screens the attraction of the nucleus and augments the energies of the valence electrons, thus favouring the establishment of normal or **di-electronic** bonds, whose ionic character is generally less important than that of the resonant or **mono-electronic** bonds.

The second remark concerns the existence of **vacancy lattices** such as that of the compound In_2Te_3 and more generally of the $III_2 VI_3$ compounds, where only one third of the tetrahedral cavities available in the close-packed array of the Column VI atoms are occupied by the atoms from Column III (as against one half in the blende structure). Such compounds cannot readily be related to the binary $III^- V^+$ or $II^{2-} VI^{2+}$ compounds because their formal charges are not balanced and the number of atoms involved is odd. An example of such lattices occurs in those intermetallic alloys which are subject to the Hume-Rothery rules, and RAYNOR [4.11] showed, for example, in relation to the Ni–Al Alloys, that the number of electrons per unit cell remains constant in the case of non-stoicheiometry by virtue of the appearance of Ni vacancies. We are prompted by this result to consider the empty site in the vacancy lattice as an atom of zero valency and we put it into the covalent formula attaching to it an index $4-$. The compound In_2Te_3 is thus written ($\square^{4-}In_2^-$) Te_3^{2+} and such a formula can readily be considered as related to that of $Zn^{2-}S^{2+}$, for example. Figures 4.3 and 4.4 show schematically the bonds resulting in the cases of In_2Te_3 and PbI_2. Such schemes are obviously symbolic and bring us back to considering the existence of a direct partial bond between the Zintl atoms.

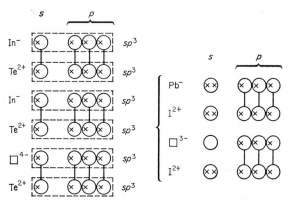

FIG. 4.3. Bond scheme   FIG. 4.4. Bond scheme in PbI_2
in In_2Te_3 (following SUCHET [4.12])

The final remark concerns the **compensated lattices,** which have been treated in Section 3.5. It is clear that it is purely a coincidence that the compound Li_3Bi obeys Mooser and Pearson's rule, although it was one of the first examples given by these authors in support of their arguments. The apparent agreement arises from the fact that the transfer of electrons from the cation CIL to the partial lattice attaches there a single electron, so that the rule may be applied to either Li_3Bi or to $[Li_2Bi]^-$. A similar confusion occurs in the case of Cs_3Sb or $[CsSb]^{2-}$. Na_3As on the other hand appears to obey the rule $n_e/n_a + b = 8$, even though the DO_{18} structure of this compound is quite incompatible with the consideration of tetrahedral bonds. However, the hypothesis of a partial lattice [NaAs] with sp^2 bonds would be consistent with the corresponding rule $n_e/n_a + b = 6$. Finally, the compounds TlSe and Bi_2Te_3 are manifestly exceptions to the rule, since their CIL has retained its valence electrons, and the disregard of the compensated lattice completely precludes an understanding of their bonds. Let us add with respect to the latter that the partial lattice $[BiTe]^+$ does not derive at all from a binary compound, but may be directly related to elements of Group V, in the way that SiC is related to the elements of Group IV. Such binary compounds or partial lattices may be considered as **pseudo-elements.**

4.4 General Classification of Semiconductors

We are now in a position to present a general classification of binary compound semiconductors and of such of the ternary and quaternary compounds as are actually known. This classification is made up of a series of tables indicating the relationships possible with the principal binary compounds. Atoms are designated by the roman numeral corresponding to their column in the periodic classification, together with the formal charge corresponding to the type of orbital used. The atoms which are admissible in the structure are presented in another column of the table. Table 4.3 is concerned with bonding by sp^3 orbitals (blend and related structures). Table 4.4 is concerned with bonding by p^3 orbitals (double layers of the SnS type, as well as rocksalt).

Table 4.5 is concerned with bonding by sp/sp^3 resonant orbitals (antifluorite and related structures). These three tables were published by the author in 1959 [4.1], together with the bibliographic references to the first studies relating to each compound. Table 4.6 brings together certain less common and less easily defined sorts of bond which we shall examine in greater detail below.

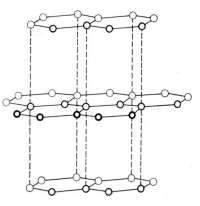

FIG. 4.5. *A9* structure for graphite

Considering for the moment the case of bonds utilizing sp^2 orbitals, one knows that graphite shows a metallic conductivity in the plane of the hexagons corresponding to the structure *A9* (Fig. 4.5) in agreement with its electronic formula s^2p^2 ($a + b = 7$, instead of 6). Boron crystallizes in a complex structure and compounds of the type $II^- IV^+$ crystallizing with

TABLE 4.3

CIL	0	I	II	III	IV	V	VI	VII	Structure	Atoms permitted in the structure	Examples
I_2^+				III^-		V^+			B3 blende	Cs-Sb	InSb
		I^{3-}				V^+			B32 'TlNa' vacancy or compensated bl.		Cs_3Sb
			II^{2-}	III^-_2	IV	V^+_2			E1 chalcopyrite	ZnCd-SiGeSn-PAs	$CdSnAs_2$
			II^{2-}				VI^{2+}_3		B3 blende		ZnS
		I^{3-}	II^{2-}_3	III^-			VI^{2+}_3		B3 blende	Cu-Cd-In-Te	$CuCdInTe_3$
		I^{3-}_2			IV		VI^{2+}_3		B3 blende	Cu-SiSn-SeTe	Cu_2SnTe_3
	$\square^{4-}$			III^-_2			VI^{2+}_3		B3 vacancy bl.	GaIn-Se-Te	In_2Te_3
			II^{2-}_4				VI^{2+}_4		E1 chalcopyrite	AgCu-AlGaInTl-SSeTe	$AgInTe_2$
		I^{3-}	II^{2-}	III^-_2			VI^{2+}_4		B3 or E3 bl. or vacancy chalco.	ZnCdHg-AlGaIn-SSeTe	$HgIn_2Te_4$
		I^{3-}_2	II^{2-}		IV		VI^{2+}_4		$H2_6$ stannite	Cu-FeNi-GeSn-SSe	Cu_2FeSnS_4
	$\square^{4-}$	I^{3-}_3				V^+	VI^{2+}_4		$H2_5$ famatite	Cu-AsSb-SSe	Cu_3SbS_4
		I^{3-}_4	II^{2-}					VII^{3+}_4	B3 blende or B2 caesium chlor.	CuAg-I / Cs-ClBrI	AgI
	$\square^{4-}$	I^{3-}_2	II^{2-}					VII^{3+}_4	B3 or E3 bl. or vacancy chalco.	CuAg-Hg-I	Cu_2-HgI_4
	$\square^{4-}_2$		II^{2-}					VII^{3+}_4	C13	Hg-I	HgI_2

TABLE 4.4

0	(I II) III IV V VI VII					Structure	Atoms permitted in the structure	Examples
	III^{2-} (I^{2-})	IV^{-}_{3}			VI^{+}_{3}	{ $A7$ arsenic or $B1$ rocksalt	GeSnPb-SSeTe	PbS
		IV^{-}	V		VI^{+}_{3}	seligmannite	Cu-Pb-As-S	CuPbAsS$_3$
		IV^{-}_{4}			VI^{+}_{4}	{ $B1$ rocksalt or $F5_6$ wolfsbergite (chalcostibite)	NaKCuAgTl-AsSbBi-S	AgSbS$_2$
	III^{2-} (I^{2-}_{2})		V_{2}		VI^{+}_{4}			
	$\square^{3-}$	IV^{-}	V_{2}		VI^{+}_{4}	{ $F5_6$ vacancy wolfsbergite	Pb-AsSb-S	PbAs$_2$S$_4$
	III^{2-}_{2}	IV^{-}	V	VI^{+}	VII^{2+} VII^{2+}_{2} VII^{2+}	'α TlI'	Tl-I	TlI
	$\square^{3-}$					$C6$ cadmium iodide	Pb-I	PbI$_2$
	$\square^{3-}$			VI^{+}		$\sim C6$	Bi-Te-BrI	BiTeBr

TABLE 4.5

CIL	0	I	II	III	IV	V	VI	VII	Structure	Atoms permitted in the structure	Examples
I^+		I	II_2						*C1* fluorite	Li-Mg-Sn	Mg$_2$Sn
		I	II		IV				*DO$_3$* 'BiF$_3$' or compensated fl. *C1b* fluorite	LiNaKAg-MgZn--AsSbBi	Li$_2$MgSn LiMgSb
I^+		I_2	II		IV	V^+			*DO$_3$* 'BiF$_3$' or compensated fl. *C1* fluorite or neighbouring structure	LiCu-SbBi	Li$_3$Bi
		I_2				V^+	VI^{2+}			LiNaKAg-SeTe	Na$_2$Se
	$\square^{2-}$	I_3	II_4 II_3	III^+	IV_2	V_2^+ V_2^+			*E9d* fluorite *D5$_3$-D5$_9$* vacancy fluorite	Li-AlGa-N BeMgZnCd-NPAs	Li$_3$GaN$_2$ Mg$_3$As$_2$
		I_5^-	II_6		IV_3 IV^{2+}	V_3^+			*C1* fluorite	Li-SiGe-NPAs	Li$_5$GeP$_3$

TABLE 4.6

C.I.L.	I	II	III	IV	V	VI	VII	Structure	Atoms permitted in the structure
I_2 . . .		II^{-}		IV^{+}	V^{2+}				Unknown
	I^{2-}							*B12* boron nitride	NaKRb-AsSbBi
		II_3		$\equiv V_3$				'CdSb'	ZnCd-Sb
	I_3^{-}				$(V) \equiv VI_3^{+}$			proustite	Ag-(AsSb)-S
	$(I^{-}\text{-}I^{-})_3$						$\equiv VII_3^{2+}$	*C6* cadmium iodide (resonance)	Ag-F
III^{+} . . .				IV		VI_2		*C6*	Sn-SSe
			III^{-}			VI_2		*B37*	Tl-Se
		II^{2-}					VII_2^{+}	*C6*	Cd-I
				IV	V			*B1* rocksalt	GeSn-PAsSb
			III^{-}			VI^{+}		'GaS'	GaIn-SSeTe

structures related to *A9* are not known. Nevertheless, this structure is known; it occurs in the *B12* structure of the hexagonal form of insulating boron-nitride BN, for which the bond scheme is uncertain. We saw in Section 3.5 that the partial lattices such as [NaAs] belonging to the DO_{18} structure of sodium arsenide had exactly the same arrangement.

The orthorhombic structures of the binary II V compounds (ZnSb and CdSb) and their bonding schemes have been discussed by MOOSER and PEARSON [4.6], [4.7] who sought to fit them to their rule. The bond angles indicated in Fig. 4.1 show, in fact, that their case is intermediate between that of bonds formed from sp^3 or p^3 orbitals. One can relate these compounds to proustite (arsenical silver blende) $Ag_3^- AsS_3^+$ and to the unusual binary compound $Ag_2^- F^{2+}$ (where the length of the Ag–F bond shows a contraction of 7% with respect to the sum of Pauling's ionic radii). In the first case, the role of the arsenic atom is restricted to establishing a *p* bond between the S atoms (corresponding to the bond between Sb atoms in CdSb), so that they do not really enter into the scheme of filiation. In the second case, one finds again the F–F bond between Zintl atoms, but the phenomenon of resonance intervenes (related to the marked ionic nature of the Ag–F bond) and leads to co-ordinations of 4 and 6 with *s* bonds between the silver atoms [4.12]. Figure 4.6 gives the bonding schemes which we propose for CdSb (*a*) and Ag_2F (*b*).

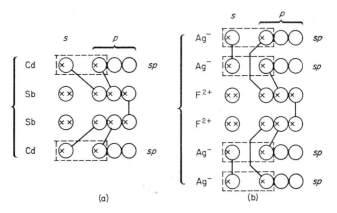

(a)   (b)

FIG. 4.6. Bond schemes in CdSb and Ag_2F (following SUCHET [4.12])

In the case of the binary IV VI_2 compounds (SnS_2 and $SnSe_2$) crystallizing in the *C6* structure of cadmium iodide, the bond scheme given in Fig. 4.4 is inapplicable, and similarly that of Fig. 4.6 (Ag_2F crystallizes in the same structure). We must consider, by analogy with silicon and germanium, deformed tetrahedra situated around the tin atoms. We can relate them to the partial lattices [III VI_2]⁻ of the binary III VI compounds (TlS and

TlSe) crystallizing in the *B37* structure (Fig. 4.2), as well as perhaps to the compound CdI_2 crystallizing initially in the *C6* structure.

The hexagonal structure of GaS and other III VI binary compounds (GaSe, GaTe, InS and InSe) is made up of quadruple laminae with a direct Ga–Ga bond. This structure is reminiscent of that of the II V binary compounds, and their semiconducting character, which has often been mentioned, has recently been considered again by FIELDING *et al.* [4.13]. We propose that these compounds should be derived from the little known IV V binary compounds GeP, SnAs, SnSb [4.5] which crystallize in the *B1* structure and GeAs [4.14]. Thus we are again concerned with a case of a co-ordination intermediate between 3 and 4.

Finally, the existence of compound semiconductors in which the bonds utilize pure *s* orbitals is not excluded and can be applied, for example, to NaAu [4.15] and CsAu [4.16]. It is not very likely that in this case a distinction can be drawn between these and the metallic alloys of similar formula. If we wish to apply rules of the type proposed by MOOSER and PEARSON to all these compounds, it is necessary to take care over the definition of n_e, which is different for each of the constituents, and over the number appearing in the right-hand term, which is fixed uniquely by the type of orbital used by the Zintl atom.

4.5 Transition Element Compounds

In passing from the simplest to the most complex atoms, following the increasing atomic numbers in the periodic classification, there is a regular increase in both the nuclear charge and the number of electrons (Fig. 4.7). These electrons are placed successively in the 1*s*, 2*s*, 2*p*, 3*s*, 3*p* energy

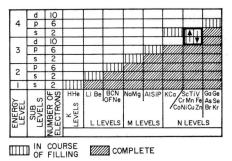

FIG. 4.7. Location of the transition elements in the periodic classification

levels, then, as a result of the screening effect produced by the eighteen electrons already distributed around the nucleus, the first two electrons which would be placed in the 3*d* level find themselves pushed up into the 4*s* level above (Fig. 1.1). After this stage, the completion of the 3*d* level with ten electrons continues, with some hesitation between the 4*s* and

$3d$ levels, and with the consequent possibility of many different valencies. The ten elements concerned are indicated by the black-edged rectangle in Fig. 4.7, and constitute the first series of transition elements.

We shall consider at first the case where the electrons belonging to the d level do not take part in the orbitals utilized. This is the usual behaviour for atoms from columns I_B and II_B, but it can also occur in the case of atoms from the group T (Table 1.1). Thus iron behaves like an element of column III_B in chalcopyrite $(Cu^{3-}Fe^-)S_2^{2+}$ and like an element of Group II_B in stannite $(Cu_2^{3-}Fe^{2-}Sn)S_4^{2+}$, titanium like an element of the fourth column in $(Li_5^-Ti^{2+})P_3^+$ and the lanthanides like elements of column III_B in the group of compounds $(\square^{4-}Ln_2^{2-})VI_3^{2+}$, [4.17]. The exchange of electrons between the d and s levels often occurs, so that the elements of the group T belonging to different columns in the periodic classification can display the same electronic formula, without there being any need to attach a formal charge to their chemical symbol. PEARSON [4.18] showed that in the $B8$ structure of nickel arsenide NiAs, where the co-ordination of 6 for each atom is similar to that for the $B1$ structure (Fig. 4.8), the d and s levels of the T atom donate to the p level the number of electrons necessary for the establishment of the formula s^0p^3. Thus we find binary TV compounds which are similar to VV pseudo-elements such as the partial lattice

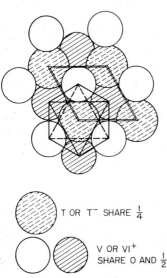

T OR T⁻ SHARE $\frac{1}{4}$

V OR VI⁺
SHARE 0 AND $\frac{1}{2}$

FIG. 4.8. $B8$ structure for nickel arsenide (following GAY [1.8])

[BiTe]⁺, except that the phenomenon of resonance now has some effect. The T⁻VI⁺ compounds are derived from these binary compounds, the exchanges d-s-p in this case giving the T atom the formula s^0p^2 which can be compared with the compounds $II_A^-VI^+$ (CaS) and IV^-VI^+ (PbS). The semiconducting character of these compounds implies that the T atoms cannot be too close in the cell and experiment shows that the *ratio c/a of the dimensions must be at least* 1·60. We propose to link with these compounds the $C6$ structure of CdI₂ (cf. for example, Fig. 4.9 for PdS₂), by considering it as a vacancy structure of the $B8$ type. Thus the notation for this compound is $(\square^{3-}T^+)S_2^+$, T representing an atom of electronic formula $d^x s^1 p^3$.

Let us now pass to the general case where the atom T forms hybrid bonds using d^2sp^3 orbitals. We shall designate these atoms by the chemical symbols for the first series of transition elements. The intention is that each of these chemical symbols may equally well represent the atoms of the second and third transition series situated in the same vertical column of the periodic classification. As we know their initial electronic formula (cf. Table 1.1), it is easy to see that each T atom will only be able to form

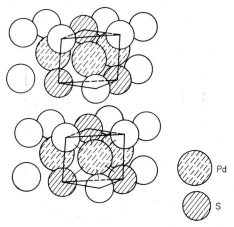

FIG. 4.9. *C6* structure for PdS$_2$

such bonds at the price of transferring electrons represented by the formal charges corresponding to formula d^8sp^3:

$$Sc^{9-}\ Ti^{8-}\ V^{7-}\ Cr^{6-}\ Mn^{5-}\ Se^{4-}\ Co^{3-}\ Ni^{2-}\ Cu^-\ Zn^0$$

The absence of compounds of the type TX is readily foreseen since the bonds are necessarily mixed and no sort of *p* or *s-p* orbital without resonance could allow a co-ordination equal to that needed for the d^2sp^3 bond. We shall now deal with compounds of the type TX$_2$ and TX$_3$ corresponding to *Strukturbericht* symbols *C* and *D*. Let us consider for the moment the

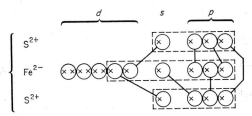

FIG. 4.10. Bond scheme in FeS$_2$

d^2sp^3/sp^3 bonds whose existence has been recognized in the *C2* structure of pyrites FeS$_2$ or Fe(S–S) (Fig. 4.10), and in the neighbouring *C18* structures (marcassite FeS$_2$) [4.19], Fl (cobaltite CoAsS) and EO$_7$ (arsenical-pyrites FeAsS). The formal charges introduced above allow the establishment of a succession PdAs$_2$–CoAsS–FeS$_2$, but it appears that the conductivity of the neighbouring compounds such as $FeAs_2$–$FeAsS$–MnS_2 cannot be metallic. In other words, electronic formulae such as $d^x sp^3$ must be possible for the transition element, where x is less than 8. The lack of experimental results does not allow greater precision. The $d^2 sp^3 / sp^3$ bond exists in both the $D2$ structure of skutterudite $CoAs_3$ and in Dudkin's compound $CoSb_3$ [4.20] (Fig. 4.11), but the other members of this family are unknown.

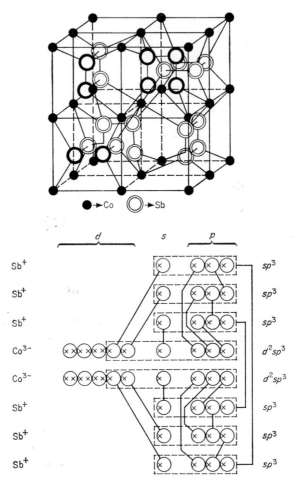

FIG. 4.11. $D2$ structure and bond scheme in $CoSb_3$
(following DUDKIN [4.20])

Other types of bonds with d-s-p orbital hybrids are possible, but appear to be less common in three-dimensional lattices. Knowing the initial electronic formula of the T atoms, we see that they can only form dsp^2 bonds for example, at the cost of electron transfers represented by formal

TABLE 4.7

Types of orbital used	Structure	Sc	Ti	V	Cr	Mn	Fe	Co	Ni	Cu	Zn	IV	V	VI	VII	Atoms permitted in the structure
p^3	{B8 nickel arsenide / B31 (MnP)} {B8 nickel arsenide / B1 rocksalt}					I'^- — T'^- — T^{2-}							V'^- — $VI'^\pm$ — $VII^{2\pm}$			CrMnFeCoNiPt-PAsSb* / CrFeCoNiPd-SSeTe* / Unknown
	C6 cadmium iodide / ditto					T^{2-} — $T'^\pm$; $\square^3$ — $\square^3$; T'^-							V_2^- — VI_2^- — VII_2^{2-}			TiVCoNi-SSeTe / TiVMnFeCo-I
d^2sp^3/sp^3	{C2 pyrites / C18 marcassite} {F1 cobaltine / E0₁ arsenical pyrite} {C2 pyrites / C18 marcassite}					$(Fe^{2-})Co^{3-}Ni^{2-}$; $Fe^{3-}\,Co^{3-}$; $Mn^{4-}Fe^{4-}$; Mn^{5-} ; C^{4-}				Cu^-	$Zn(IV-IV)$	$(IV-V)^+$	$(V-V)^{2+}$; $(V-VI)^{3+}$; $(VI-VI)^{4+}$; $(VI-VII)^{5+}$; $(VII-VII)^{4+}$			Unknown / Unknown / FeNiPd-PAsSb / FeCo-AsSb-S / MnFeRuOs-SSeTe / Unknown / Unknown
	D2 skutterudite					Ni^{2-} ; Co^{3-} ; Fe^{4-}						IV	$V_2^\pm$; $V_3^\pm$; V_2^+ — $VI^{2\pm}$			Unknown / Co-AsSb / Unknown
dsp^2/sp^3	{B17 cooperite / B34 (PdSe)}					Ni^{2-} ; Co^{3-}				Cu^-	Zn	IV	$V'^\pm$ — $VI^{2\pm}$ — $VII^{3\pm}$			Unknown / PdPt-OSSe / Unknown

* Subject to the condition $c/a > 1{\cdot}60$

charges identical to those relative to d^2sp^3 (respective formulae d^9sp^2 and d^8sp^3, namely 11 d, s or p electrons in both cases). The four coplanar bonds of the dsp^2 bond are found in the *B17* structure of PdO and of PtS, cooperite (Fig. 4.12), and in the related *B34* structure of PdS and PdSe.

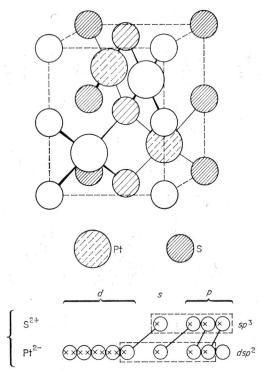

FIG. 4.12. *B17* structure and bond scheme in PtS

Table 4.7 summarizes the above discussion.

It is hardly possible to apply Mooser and Pearson's rule to the prediction of the semiconducting nature of compounds of the transition elements, since *the number of valence electrons able to take part in the covalent bonds compatible with the type of crystal structure* (cf. Section 4.2) *could not be fixed* a priori. Counting up all the *d*, *s* and *p* electrons on the T atoms, produces the inequality $a + b \geqslant 2c$. Thus these rules can only be applied when the covalent scheme of the compound is definitely known [4.21]. We shall return to these questions in a more rigorous manner in Chapter 8.

Chapter 5

CERAMIC OXIDE SEMICONDUCTORS*

5.1 Transition Metal Oxides

IN Chapter 2 we saw that the presence of physical defects (vacancies and interstitials) in ionic crystals such as the oxides allows one of the mechanisms by which semiconductivity may appear. Although we illustrated this mechanism only in the case of those vacancies most frequently found in the alkali halides, interstitials naturally give rise to analogous centres. Thus, in the case of zinc oxide, an interstitial Zn atom must, in the absence of anions in similar sites, itself ensure its neutrality. Because of the large dielectric constant of the surroundings, ionization occurs and the two valence electrons are partially freed (Fig. 5.1). Defect zinc oxide has for its formula in Rees' notation:

$$Zn^{2+}(Zn_x^{2+} e_{2x}^- / \triangle)O^{2-}$$

A large concentration of donor centres can be obtained with this oxide, but this is somewhat exceptional and the alkaline-earth oxides, for example, give smaller concentrations and have very small electrical conductivities.

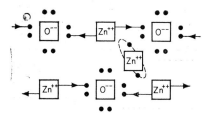

FIG. 5.1. Effect of an interstitial cation in ZnO

The concentration of defects, and thereby the conductivity, may be greatly increased in the case of the transition metal oxides, where the mechanism of semiconductivity is slightly different. We saw in Section 4.5 that the exchange of electrons between d and s levels was possible, for example between $3d$ and $4s$ levels for the first series of transition metals (Fig. 4.7). Table 5.1 (following [5.1]) gives the electronic structure of the

* Ionic formulae are used systematically in this chapter, cf. ref. [5.1].

TABLE 5.1

Neutral atom	Number of electrons in 3d level	Number of electrons in level 4	Corresponding cation (*complete ionization*)	Stability (*oxides*)
Sc^0	0 1	3 2	⟨Sc^{3+}⟩ Sc^{2+}	↓
Ti^0	0 1 2	4 3 2	⟨Ti^{4+}⟩ Ti^{3+} Ti^{2+}	↓
V^0	0 1 2 3	5 4 3 2	⟨V^{5+}⟩ V^{4+} V^{3+} V^{2+}	↓
Cr^0	0 1 2 3 4 5	6 5 4 3 2 1	Cr^{6+} Cr^{5+} Cr^{4+} ⟨Cr^{3+}⟩ Cr^{2+}	↑
Mn^0	3 4 5	4 3 2	⟨Mn^{4+}⟩ Mn^{3+} Mn^{2+}	↓
Fe^0	4 5 6	4 3 2	Fe^{4+} ⟨Fe^{3+}⟩ Fe^{2+}	↓
Co^0	6 7	3 2	Co^{3+} ⟨Co^{2+}⟩	↑
Ni^0	7 8	3 2	Ni^{3+} ⟨Ni^{2+}⟩	↑
Cu^0	9 10	2 1	Cu^{2+} ⟨Cu^{+}⟩	↑
Zn^0	10	2	⟨Zn^{2+}⟩	

various cations which may be formed from the neutral atom. As a general rule one can state that the instability of electrons situated in the $3d$ level when the $4s$ level is empty is just as great for the ions as for the atoms. The state of ionization shown for the initial entries corresponds to complete emptying of the $3d$ level and, for the following atoms, the stable cation (enclosed in a circle) generally has a less well-filled $3d$ level than the neutral atom. A knowledge of the successive ionization energies, the electronic formulae and the crystal cell allows us to forecast approximately the behaviour of their oxides [5.1] (cf. also [1]).

The modified mechanism of semiconduction is characterized by the absence of partially free charge carriers, e^- and p^+, such as those considered for colour centres in the alkali halides. An interstitial cation or the reverse, a cation vacancy, which we wrote

$$M^{2+}_{1-x}(M^{2+}_x \, e^-_{2x}/\triangle)O^{2-}$$

$$(M^{2+}_{1-x}p^+_{2x}/\boxplus)O^{2-}$$

may alternatively be written

$$(M^{2+}_{1-x}M^+_x/\boxplus)(M^+_x/\triangle)O^{2-}$$

$$(M^{2+}_{1-3x}M^{3+}_{2x}/\boxplus)O^{2-}$$

In other words, the cation M^{2+} can take up either the electron e^- by transferring one of its $4s$ electrons to the $3d$ level or a hole p^+ with the inverse transfer. The groups $M^{2+}e^-$ and $M^{2+}p^+$ thus become simply M^+ and M^{3+}. The neutrality of the crystal does not require that the ions in the state M^+ (or M^{3+}) occupy fixed positions, but simply that their concentration remains constant with respect to that of the interstitials (or the vacancies). Under the effect of an electric field the excess electron of the M^+ cation can thus pass to a neighbouring cation and so be displaced step by step (n-type). In just the same manner the hole existing on a M^{3+} cation can pass to a neighbouring cation (p-type). VERWEY [5.2], however, showed that *such conductivity could only take place if metallic ions of the same element, in states of ionization differing by one unit, occupied equivalent crystallographic sites.* Figure 5.2 illustrates the case of the cations occupying the normal lattice sites. Figure 5.3 shows the states of ionization in non-stoicheiometric nickel oxide.

The passage M^{2+}—M^+ or M^{2+}—M^{3+} is not always possible, as is shown in Table 5.1. The formation of a Zn^+ ion, for example, could take place (formula $d^{10}s^1$), but would not have the stability which would be given to it by the (impossible) simultaneous passage of an s electron into the already saturated d level. Although theoretically possible, these interchanges do not always occur, and in particular, the two types rarely occur simultaneously. In other words, certain oxides favour becoming n-type semiconductors, whilst others favour becoming p-type semiconductors. Table

5.2 (following [5.1]) indicates the factors which determine this behaviour: the successive ionization energies expressed in electron volts, and, in parentheses, the ionic radii in Ångströms, following [3] (cf. Chapter 6). The values enclosed in a circle correspond to the most stable states of ionization under normal conditions. The cases immediately below the upper stepped line (Sc^{3+}, Ti^{4+}, V^{5+}) correspond to a full $3p$ level and an empty $3d$ level, those immediately below the lower stepped line (Cu^+, Zn^{2+}) correspond to a full $3d$ level and an empty $4s$ level.

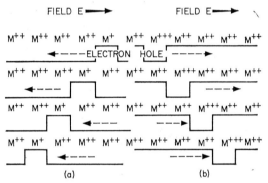

FIG. 5.2. Mechanism of semiconductivity

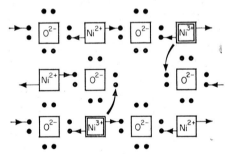

FIG. 5.3. Effect of a Ni vacancy in NiO

Let us consider for the moment the three members Sc^{3+}, Ti^{4+} and V^{5+}. The removal of an additional electron could only be made via the $3p$ level, and clearly would require a much higher ionization energy. Thus a variation in the state of ionization can only be made by reduction to Sc^{2+}, Ti^{3+} and V^{4+}, as confirmed by experiment [5.3]. Moreover, the ionic radii are small, at least in the case of $Ti^{4+} = 0.68$ Å and $V^{5+} = 0.50$ Å, allowing us to foresee their ready passage into an interstitial position. As for the latter members, Co^{2+}, Ni^{2+} and Cu^+, the instability of the $3d$ electrons already noted permits us to foresee their tendency to oxidation to Co^{3+}, Ni^{3+} and Cu^{2+}. We may note that the particularly high ionic radius for the copper

TABLE 5.2

Element	I	II	III	IV	V	VI	VII
K	4·3 (1·33)	32	46	61			
Ca	6·1	12 (0·99)	51	70			
Sc	6·7	13 ← ⟨25⟩ n (0·78)		74	97		
Ti	6·8	14	28 ← ⟨43⟩ n (0·68)	100			
V	6·7	14	26	48 ← ⟨65⟩ n (0·50)	133		
Cr	6·7	17	⟨27⟩ → (0·55) p	51	73	(0·45)	
Mn	7·4	16 (0·80)	34 ← ⟨54⟩ n		76		(0·35)
Fe	7·8	16 ← ⟨31⟩ (0·75) n (0·53)		56			
Co	7·8	⟨17⟩ → 34 (0·72) p		53			
Ni	7·6	⟨18⟩ → 36 (0·68) p		56			
Cu	⟨7·7⟩ → (0·95)	20 p(0·69)	29	59			
Zn	9·4	18 (0·70)	40	62			
Ga	6·0	20	31 (0·60)	64			
Ge	8·1	16	34	45 (0·54)	93		

Transition elements

ion $Cu^+ = 0.95$ Å, and the compact structure of cuprite completely precludes its passage into an interstitial position. The situation is less clear for the intermediate cases (Cr^{3+}, Mn^{4+} and Fe^{3+}), and experimental results show that the oxides Cr_2O_3 and Fe_2O_3—although isomorphous with the corundum structure—display opposite behaviours between 500 and 1000°C [5.4]; Cr_2O_3 becomes a semiconductor by oxidation (cation Cr^{3+} vacancies with the appearance of Cr^{4+} ions), and Fe_2O_3 becomes a semiconductor by reduction. It will be seen in the next section that, under certain conditions, each of these oxides can form n- and p-type semiconductors.

5.2 Magnetite. Valence Induction

In the preceding section we saw that the presence of metallic ions in different states of ionization can lead to semiconduction. This condition is realized in the oxides of the transition elements containing suitable defects, such as interstitial cations for titanium and vanadium oxides, or cation vacancies for nickel and copper oxides. Certain crystals fulfil these conditions in the absence of structural defects, and the most important of these is magnetite Fe_3O_4. The cubic structure of magnetite is analogous to that of a spinel such as $MgAl_2O_4$, where, for every two octahedral cavities occupied by trivalent cations, one tetrahedral cavity is occupied by a divalent cation, that is (cf. Section 1.4):

$$(Mg^{2+}/\boxplus_t)(Al^{3+}/\boxplus_o)_2O_4^{2-} \quad \text{(Fig. 5.4)}$$

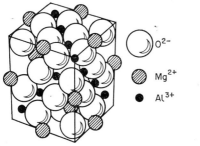

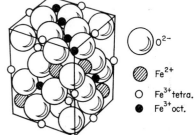

FIG. 5.4. Spinel structure $MgAl_2O_4$ FIG. 5.5. Magnetite structure Fe_3O_4

However, magnetite shares one peculiarity with the magnetic ferrites. An iron cation Fe^{3+} occupies the tetrahedral cavity, whilst the two octahedral occupied cavities share the remaining Fe^{3+} cation and the Fe^{2+} cation [5.5]:

$$(Fe^{3+}/\boxplus_t)(Fe^{3+}Fe^{2+}/\boxplus_o)O_4^{2-} \quad \text{(Fig. 5.5)}$$

The ferrous and ferric ions are thus found alternating regularly in the octahedral cavities in equivalent and adjacent crystallographic sites, thus accounting for the exceptionally low resistivity of this oxide.

Although the conductivity of magnetite is thus explicable in terms of the presence of Fe^{3+} and Fe^{2+} cations, it is nevertheless different from that of hematite Fe_2O_3 containing iron interstitial cations or oxygen vacancies. In the former case it is impossible to specify the type (n or p) of charge carriers since both sorts of cation exist in equivalent quantities, and the electrical current is transported simultaneously by electrons and holes (intrinsic conductivity). On the contrary, in the case of hematite, we have only electrons (n-type). In solid solutions of magnetite with insulating spinels such as $MgAl_2O_4$, the dilution increases the mean interionic distance between Fe^{3+} and Fe^{2+}, with a consequent diminution of the conductivity. Magnetite is not the only oxide containing metallic cations in different states of ionization, and it is interesting briefly to consider analogous oxides. Cobalt oxide Co_3O_4 has a normal spinel structure like that of $MgAl_2O_4$:

$$(Co^{2+}/\boxplus_t)(Co^{3+}/\boxplus_o)_2O_4^{2-}$$

Thus the Co^{2+} and Co^{3+} ions are found in different crystallographic sites, which accounts for the very high resistivity of this oxide. Haussmannite Mn_3O_4 has a deformed spinel structure (tetragonal), in which two types of crystallographic site are found corresponding to the tetrahedral and octahedral cavities of the spinel structure. This structure presents certain analogies with that of magnetite:

$$(Mn^{2+}/\boxplus_t)(Mn^{4+}Mn^{2+}/\boxplus_o)O_4^{2-}$$

The large resistivity of this oxide (10^7 ohm-cm) shows that the exchange of electrons or holes between the cations of the same element, in states of ionization differing by two units, cannot lead to semiconductivity, even if these cations occupy equivalent crystallographic sites.

It is possible to make crystals where the semiconductivity, as in the case of magnetite, is independent of the presence of vacancies and interstitials. In Section 2.2 we alluded to impurities in ionic crystals, and it is clear that these produce, in the same way as a physical defect, an electrical perturbation if their state of ionization differs from that of the normal ions in the lattice. Suppose that an oxide having a stable valency such as L_2O is added in small quantity to the oxide MO of a transition metal which will readily take up excess oxygen and which can form with it a solid solution by sintering or fusion. In the case of an M^{2+} cation vacancy, we saw in the preceding section that the two neighbouring cations passed into the M^{3+} state in order to re-establish the electrical neutrality of the crystal. Here, on the other hand, only one cation will change its state of ionization:

$$(M_{1-2x}^{2+}M_x^{3+}L_x^+/\boxplus)O^{2-}$$

The essential difference is that in the first case we had an excess of oxygen anions with respect to the metal cations, whilst in the second case their numbers are rigorously identical. We shall say that such semiconductivity is obtained by **valence induction** of the L_2O oxide upon the MO oxide, there being no need for structural defects in the latter. It is clear nevertheless that defects will be present, as in all crystals, but the phenomenon of semiconductivity is no longer dependent upon them, and it is possible to obtain much greater concentrations of impurities than of physical defects.

The phenomenon of valence induction, whose discovery is due to VERWEY and his co-workers [5.6], hence requires the following conditions:

(*a*) The basic material be a transition metal compound whose cations are able to adopt several states of ionization; the conditions of preparation be such that the formation of defects hindering the change of state of the cations is prevented (cf. following section).

(*b*) The material added be a compound of a metal whose valency differs by unity from the normal valency of the metal of the basic material, the anions being common. It is desirable that a metal with stable valency be employed as additive, but experiments indicate that valence induction can often be obtained by the addition of a transition metal compound (for example, the addition of TiO_2 to Fe_2O_3).

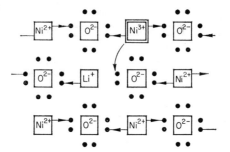

FIG. 5.6. Valence induction of Li_2O in NiO

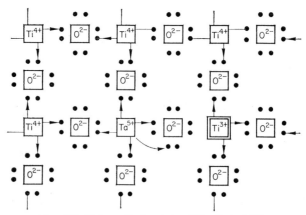

FIG. 5.7. Valence induction of Ta_2O_5 in TiO_2

The valency of the added cation will be less than that of the basic cation if the latter tends to take a higher valency (p-type), and reciprocally.

Example: Li^+ added to Ni^{2+}, Fig. 5.6.

$\qquad$ Ta^{5+} added to Ti^{4+}, Fig. 5.7.

(c) The material added must form a solid solution with the basic material, which requires that the ionic radii are not too different and that only a limited quantity of material is added. This limit is all the higher when the ionic radii are similar. Thus, in the case of the valence induction of NiO by Li_2O (radius Li^+ = radius Ni^{2+}), a concentration of up to 30% of Li^+ ions can be reached before separation into two phases occurs.

Some examples are given below of crystals (deliberately limited to the oxides) showing semiconductivity due to valence induction. Rees' notation is not indispensable, as long as we know the mechanism. In the first three the added cation and the basic cation are able to occupy equivalent crystallographic sites:

(1) In the *B1* rocksalt structure:

$$Li_x^+ Ni_{1-2x}^{2+} Ni_x^{3+} O^{2-} \quad \text{or} \quad Li_x^+ Co_{1-2x}^{2+} Co_x^{3+} O^{2-}$$

(2) In the *H1₁* spinel structure:

$$(Li_x^+ Co_{1-2x}^{2+} Co_x^{3+})_{tetr.} (Co_2^{3+})_{oct,} O_4^{2-}$$

(3) In the *C4* rutile structure:

$$Ta_x^{5+} Ti_{1-2x}^{4+} Ti_x^{3+} O_2^{2-} \quad \text{or} \quad Sb_x^{5+} Zr_{1-2x}^{4+} Zr_x^{3+} O_2^{2-}$$

In the following three cases the added and basic cations occupy different crystallographic sites:

(4) In the *G5* perovskite structure

$$(La_x^{3+} Ca_{1-x}^{2+})(Ti_{1-x}^{4+} Ti_x^{3+})O_3^{2-}, \quad (La_x^{3+} Sr_{1-x}^{2+})(Ti_{1-x}^{4+} Ti_x^{3+})O_3^{2-}$$

$$(La_x^{3+} Ba_{1-x}^{2+})(Ti_{1-x}^{4+} Ti_x^{3+})O_3^{2-} \quad \text{or} \quad (Sr_x^{2+} La_{1-x}^{3+})(Mn_{1-x}^{3+} Mn_x^{4+})O_3^{2-}$$

(5) In the *H1₁* spinel structure:

$$(Al_x^{3+} Mg_{2-x}^{2+})(Ti_{1-x}^{4+} Ti_x^{3+})O_4^{2-}$$

or $\qquad$ $(Cr_x^{3+} Mg_{2-x}^{2+})(Ti_{1-x}^{4+} Ti_x^{3+})O_4^{2-}$

(6) In the *HO₆* structure of magnesium tungstate:

$$(Cr_x^{3+} Mg_{1-x}^{2+})(W_{1-x}^{6+} W_x^{5+})O_4^{2-}$$

The apparent difference between behaviour of Fe_2O_3 (n-type) and Cr_2O_3 (p-type) is suppressed by the process of valence induction. Thus Fe_2O_3 can display n- and p-type conductivities respectively in the two compounds:

$$Ti_x^{4+} Fe_{2-2x}^{3+} Fe_x^{2+} O_3^{2-} \quad \text{and} \quad (Ba_x^{2+} La_{1-x}^{3+})(Fe_{1-x}^{3+} Fe_x^{4+})O_3^{2-}$$

5.3 Granular Structures with Surface Layers

We now shall consider qualitatively the effect on a single crystal of raising and then lowering the temperature in a specific atmosphere. The laws of diffusion in solids were reviewed in Section 3.1. They allow such an annealing process to be considered in five stages:

(a) Temperatures below $0 \cdot 3 \, T_f°\mathrm{K}$: diffusion negligible.

(b) Temperatures lying between $0 \cdot 3$ and $0 \cdot 5 \, T_f°\mathrm{K}$: chemisorption at the surface of the crystal lattice giving rise to Schottky defects. Appearance of a surface conductivity and of a concentration gradient.

(c) Temperatures lying between $0 \cdot 5$ and $T_f°\mathrm{K}$: diffusion into the crystal of defects created at the surface in stage b. Appearance of new Schottky and Frenkel defects at the surface and within the bulk.

(d) Temperatures lying between $0 \cdot 3$ and $0 \cdot 5 \, T_f°\mathrm{K}$: arrest of all diffusion within the crystals. The defects appearing at stage c find themselves 'frozen in'. However, the surface remains in equilibrium with the ambient atmosphere and by consequence, the concentration of defects at it diminishes.

(e) Temperatures below $0 \cdot 3 \, T_f°\mathrm{K}$: diffusion negligible.

Two conclusions may be drawn from this analysis: on the one hand, the atmosphere plays an important role during the course of the annealing by participating, by virtue of chemisorption, in the creation of surface defects which then diffuse into the bulk. This role will be better understood by examining the examples illustrated in Figs. 5.8 and 5.9. The first is that of titanium oxide TiO_2 annealed in a reducing atmosphere of hydrogen. It shows the chemisorption of H^+ commencing at about 400°C, the elimination of water molecules with the creation of O^{2-} anion vacancies, and then at about 800°C the appearance within the bulk of Frenkel defects whose vacancies vanish at the surface. The second is that of copper oxide Cu_2O annealed in air. It shows the chemisorption of O^{2-} commencing at about 200°C and the diffusion of Cu^+ cation vacancies from around 500°C. Moreover, this analysis also demonstrates that the concentration of defects at the surface of the crystal and within its bulk will not be identical. In general the concentration of defects within the bulk of the crystal results from a thermal equilibrium established at a temperature greater than the Tammann temperature $T_m = 0 \cdot 5 \, T_f°\mathrm{K}$, and frozen in during the cooling. The concentration of defects at the surface results from an equilibrium established during cooling from this temperature, and further lowering of the temperature prevents their diffusion to the interior. Thus the surface regions of the crystals will generally be less conducting than their bulk, since the concentration of defects follows a law of the form $\exp(-W/2kT)$. However, this mechanism can be inhibited (as with NiO, whose dissociation at high temperatures creates anion vacancies and thus diminishes the

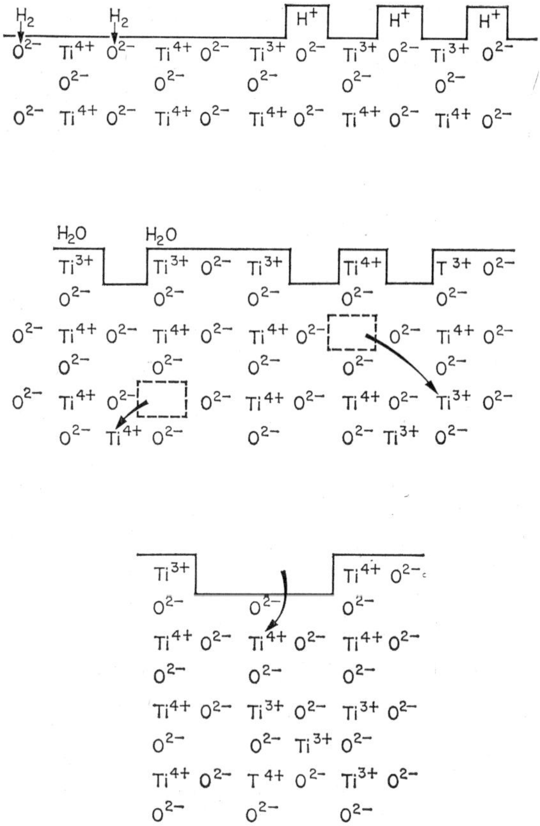

Fig. 5.8 (TiO₂ thermal cycle):

Top panel:
H_2 ... H_2 ... H^+ | H^+ | H^+
O^{2-} Ti^{4+} O^{2-} Ti^{4+} O^{2-} Ti^{3+} O^{2-} Ti^{3+} O^{2-} Ti^{3+} O^{2-}
O^{2-} O^{2-} O^{2-} O^{2-} O^{2-}
O^{2-} Ti^{4+} O^{2-} Ti^{4+} O^{2-} Ti^{4+} O^{2-} Ti^{4+} O^{2-} Ti^{4+} O^{2-}

Middle panel:
H_2O ... H_2O
Ti^{3+} | Ti^{3+} O^{2-} Ti^{3+} | Ti^{4+} | T^{3+} O^{2-}
O^{2-} O^{2-} O^{2-} O^{2-} O^{2-}
O^{2-} Ti^{4+} O^{2-} Ti^{4+} O^{2-} Ti^{4+} O^{2-} ⌐ O^{2-} Ti^{4+} O^{2-}
O^{2-} O^{2-} O^{2-} O^{2-} O^{2-}
O^{2-} Ti^{4+} O^{2-} ⌐ O^{2-} Ti^{4+} O^{2-} Ti^{4+} O^{2-} Ti^{3+} O^{2-}
O^{2-} Ti^{4+} O^{2-} O^{2-} O^{2-} Ti^{3+} O^{2-}

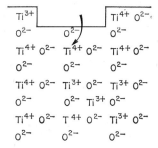

Bottom panel:
Ti^{3+} | Ti^{4+} O^{2-}
O^{2-} O^{2-} O^{2-}
Ti^{4+} O^{2-} Ti^{4+} O^{2-} Ti^{4+} O^{2-}
O^{2-} O^{2-} O^{2-}
Ti^{4+} O^{2-} Ti^{3+} O^{2-} Ti^{3+} O^{2-}
O^{2-} O^{2-} Ti^{3+} O^{2-}
Ti^{4+} O^{2-} T^{4+} O^{2-} Ti^{3+} O^{2-}
O^{2-} O^{2-} O^{2-}

FIG. 5.8. Phenomena accompanying a thermal cycle in TiO₂
(following SUCHET [5.1.])

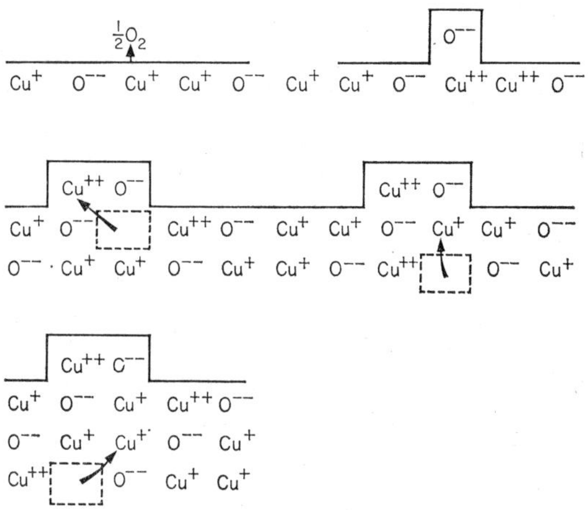

Fig. 5.9 (Cu₂O thermal cycle):

Top panel:
$\frac{1}{2}O_2$ ... O^{--}
Cu^+ O^{--} Cu^+ Cu^+ O^{--} Cu^+ Cu^+ O^{--} Cu^{++} Cu^{++} O^{--}

Middle panel:
Cu^{++} O^{--} ... Cu^{++} O^{--}
Cu^+ O^{--} Cu^{++} O^{--} Cu^+ Cu^+ O^{--} Cu^+ Cu^+ O^{--}
O^{--} · Cu^+ Cu^+ O^{--} Cu^+ Cu^+ O^{--} Cu^{++} O^{--} Cu^+

Bottom panel:
Cu^{++} O^{--}
Cu^+ O^{--} Cu^+ Cu^{++} O^{--}
O^{--} Cu^+ Cu^+ O^{--} Cu^+
Cu^{++} O^{--} Cu^+ Cu^+

FIG. 5.9. Phenomena accompanying a thermal cycle in Cu₂O
(following SUCHET [5.1])

number of acceptor centres which arise from Ni vacancies), or reinforced (as in the case of TiO_2 heated in a reducing atmosphere but put into air during the cooling, with the consequent formation of an insulating skin).

The importance of such considerations arises from the fact that these oxides are very rarely prepared or used in the form of single crystals. They are generally powdered, shaped under pressure with an organic binder, and annealed at a high temperature. This special baking is called **sintering.** It ensures simultaneously the appearance of defects in the crystal structure of each grain, the cohesion of the ensemble by the welding of the different grains, and the formation of a required shape by means of the shrinkage which accompanies this welding and the elimination of the binder. Even if two adjacent crystallites are firmly welded, a region of non-uniform chemical composition and irregular interatomic distance will always separate them, where the diffusion of the gas forming the atmosphere used during firing will have been very much easier. In any case the density never attains its theoretical value and this dilatation demonstrates that every grain or crystallite more or less conserves its individuality. The analysis of the phenomena occurring in the course of the preparation of a ceramic material thus requires a knowledge of the structure and dimensions of the crystallites employed. The process of chemisorption at the intergrain surfaces and the average time for vacancy diffusion will depend on these details.

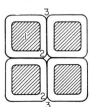

The importance of the heterogeneous structure of these ceramics will be all the more marked if the shrinkage occurring after firing is less than the maximum shrinkage possible and if re-crystallization is only slight. The surface/volume ratio of the assembly will then be a maximum.

In 1955 the author suggested the term **granular structures** with surface layers to describe such ceramics. Figure 5.10 gives a diagrammatical explanation, where equilibrium with the atmosphere has been

FIG. 5.10. Model of a granular structure

established for region 1 at a temperature $T > T_m$ and for region 2 at a temperature $T < T_m$; region 3 represents the pores in the substance. The electrical behaviour of such a heterogeneous model depends upon the type of conductivity toward which the oxide tends and upon the atmosphere in which it is fired. Let us consider for a moment the unusual example of NiO fired in air, which gives a p-type semiconductor with a surface conducting layer. If ρ_1 and ρ_2 are the resistivities of the regions 1 and 2, the equivalent electrical model below is that shown in Fig. 5.11a and the d.c. resistance of a grain is:

$$r = r_1 r_2/(r_1 + r_2) + r_3$$

with: $r_1 = k_1\rho_1, \quad r_2 = k_2\rho_2 \quad \text{and} \quad r_3 = k_3\rho_2$

where k_1, k_2 and k_3 are dimensional factors and the final term r_3 is generally negligible. If the variations of ρ_1 and ρ_2 with temperature follow the classical exponential law $\rho = A \exp (B/T)$, then the resistance of this ceramic has the form $r = A'T^b \exp (B'/T)$, with $b < 0$ [5.7]. Let us now

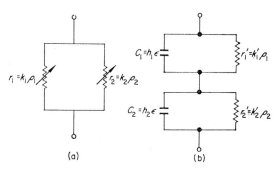

(a)   (b)

FIG. 5.11. Electrical equivalent circuits for a granular structure

pass to the case of TiO_2 fired in hydrogen and cooled in air—a process which gives an n-type semiconductor with an insulating surface layer. If ε is the permittivity of the oxide, supposedly uniform, the equivalent electrical model is that shown in Fig. 5.11b and the equivalent capacities which appear there are $c_1 = h_1\varepsilon$ and $c_2 = h_2\varepsilon$, the first usually being very small. It can be shown that at very high and very low frequencies, f and f' respectively, the apparent resistivities and permittivities for this ceramic are:

$$\rho(f) = \rho_1 \qquad \varepsilon(f) = \varepsilon$$
$$\rho(f') = x\rho_2 + \rho_1 \quad \varepsilon(f') = \varepsilon(x\rho_2^2 + \rho_1^2)/(x\rho_2 + \rho_1)^2$$

(x is the ratio of the thickness of the surface layer to the diameter of the grain) and hence there is a dispersion region for these quantities [5.8].

These phenomena are important in the application of oxide semiconductors. We shall first mention their use for negative temperature coefficient resistors, or **thermistors,** and then in the following section we shall consider the magnetic ferrites. Two principal materials are used in the manufacture of thermistors; first, the manganites $NiMn_2O_4$ and $Ni_{0.5} Co_{0.5} Mn_2O_4$, which behave like the oxides NiO and CoO, and in which the acceptor centres arise from the Ni vacancies which result in some Ni^{2+} cations passing into the state Ni^{3+}; secondly, hematite Fe_2O_3 with valence induction by TiO^2, where the donor centres arise from the Ti^{4+} cations which cause some Fe^{3+} cations to pass into the Fe^{2+} state. The large negative temperature coefficients α which can be obtained with the former materials arise from the law $\rho = AT^b \exp (B/T)$ cited previously, where the term b can reach -5 in the temperature region of interest for suitable grain sizes and sintering. The large negative values of b allow one to compensate a little for the rapid decrease of $\alpha = (b/T - B/T^2)$ as the temperature increases. Thus, for a value of α such as $-5\%/°C$ at 25°C, a value of b of -5 allows one to retain up to 150°C an α of $-2\cdot9\%/°C$ rather than $-2\cdot4\%/°C$ when $b = +0\cdot75$ [5.7]. The second group of materials, for which b is sensibly zero, display in compensation very curious variations of the apparent values of ρ and ε in terms of the firing temperature [5.9]. Figure 5.12 shows such a variation for a hematite whose grains have a diameter of a few microns and a concentration of titanium oxide of $0\cdot5\%$ molar. Region A corresponds to the chemisorption of oxygen on the surface of the grains during cooling. In region B, calculation of the ratio:

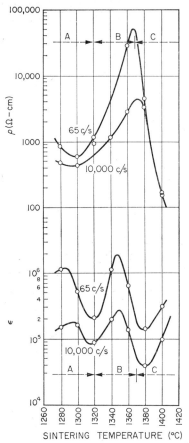

FIG. 5.12. Variation of ρ and ε as a function of the sintering temperature (following SUCHET [5.9])

$$x = [\varepsilon(f)/\varepsilon(f')].[1 - \rho(f)/\rho(f')]^2$$

shows that the latter will increase by a factor 10 when the firing temperature is increased from 1320 to 1360°C, thus demonstrating the formation of a significant layer of insulating oxides around each grain during cooling:

$$Ti_x^{4+}Fe_{1-2x}^{3+}Fe_x^{2+}O_3^{2-} + (x/4)O_2 \rightarrow Ti_x^{4+}Fe_{1-x}^{3+}O_{3+x/2}^{2-}$$

Finally, X-ray analysis indicates the appearance of a cubic second phase for firing temperatures of 1400°C and the ceramics are slightly magnetic. Zone C thus corresponds to the appearance of magnetite Fe_3O_4 at high temperatures, from the irreversible dissociation of hematite, whence the rapid decrease of ρ:

$$3Fe_2^{3+}O_3^{2-} \rightarrow 2(Fe^{3+}/\boxplus_t)(Fe^{3+}Fe^{2+}/\boxplus_o)O_4^{2-} + 0\cdot5O_2$$

5.4 Semiconducting Magnetic Ferrites

It has been shown in Section 1.4 that close-packed cubic arrangements (f.c.c.) of large anions can yield two simple structures according to the nature of the cavities occupied by the cations; the $C1$ structure (antifluorite) when the latter fill the tetrahedral cavities, and the *B1* (rocksalt) structure when they fill the octahedral cavities. Amongst the numerous complex structures where several sorts of cations are involved we cited the important example of the spinel $MgAl_2O_4$ where the Al^{3+} cations occupy the (*o*) sites, conforming with the ratio r_M/r_X; the Mg^{2+} cations, however, are unusually located in the (*t*) sites. Figure 5.13 represents this structure; the large spheres are the oxygen anions, the small, shaded spheres are the cations in octahedral sites and the small, unshaded spheres those in the tetrahedral sites. There are twice as many ions in the (*o*) sites as in the (*t*) sites, even though the latter are twice as numerous. FORESTIER

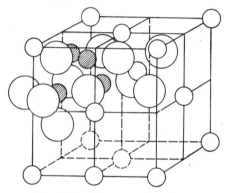

FIG. 5.13. Structure of ferrites

[5.10] showed that the substituted derivatives of magnetite or **ferrites** MFe_2O_4 crystallized in the spinel structure if $r_M/r_O < 0.62$ (transition cations) and in a hexagonal close-packed structure for ratios greater than 0.96 (alkaline-earth cations), both forms being able to co-exist for intermediate ratios.

The interest which the transition metal ferrites present arises from their magnetic properties, and the names of SNOEK [5.11], NÉEL [5.12], GUILLAUD [5.13], GORTER [5.14], etc. are notable in the study of these properties. Each of the cations is in effect a small magnet, the value of the magnetic moment being, for example:

Cations:	Fe^{3+}	Mn^{2+}	Fe^{2+}	Co^{2+}	Ni^{2+}	Cu^+	Zn^{2+}
Moment (in Bohr magnetons):	5.0	5.0	4.4	3.7	2.3	1.1	0

The structure contains two sub-lattices for the magnetic ions; the sub-lattice *A* (tetrahedral sites), and the sub-lattice *B* (octahedral sites). Experiment shows that the ferrite $ZnFe_2O_4$ has the normal spinel structure:

$$(Zn^{2+})_t \overrightarrow{(Fe^{3+})_o} \overleftarrow{(Fe^{3+})_o} O_4$$

and the moments of the ions on the B sub-lattice exactly cancel one another in pairs, as indicated by the arrows; thus the ferrite is paramagnetic. On the contrary, in ferrites where other cations intervene we have an inverse spinel structure:

$$\overrightarrow{(Fe^{3+})_t}\overleftarrow{(M^{2+}Fe^{3+})_o}O_4$$

in which the moments of the ions on the B sub-lattice are parallel with one another, and oppose those on the A sub-lattice. The resulting moment is thus equal to that of the M^{2+} ion, being:

Ferrite:	$MnFe_2O_4$	$FeFe_2O_4$	$CoFe_2O_4$	$NiFe_2O_4$	$CuFe_2O_4$
Moment (magnetons):	5·0	4·4	3·7	2·3	1·1

This particular sort of magnetism has been called ferrimagnetism by Néel. When one prepares a mixed ferrite:

$$ZnFe_2O_4/MFe_2O_4,$$

one obtains a structure intermediate between the normal and inverse spinels:

$$\overrightarrow{(Zn_x^{2+}Fe_{1-x}^{3+})_t}\overleftarrow{(M_{1-x}^{2+}Fe_{1+x}^{3+})_o}O_4$$

$$\overleftarrow{---}\overrightarrow{(Fe_x^{3+}Zn_{1-x}^{2+})_t}\overleftarrow{(M_x^{2+}Fe_{1-x}^{3+})_o(Fe^{3+})_o}O_4$$

whose resultant magnetic moment may be appreciable if the zinc concentration in the ferrite is not too large.

The same reasons which commend the ferrites as materials for magnetic cores for use at high frequencies in telecommunication systems likewise assure the success of the mixed manganese-zinc ferrites and of the nickel-zinc ferrites. The large magnetic permeability attained in the former requires the presence of a small quantity of magnetite Fe_3O_4 which reduces their resistivity to the order of an ohm-cm [5.15], whilst the resistivity of the second remains of the order of 10^4 ohm-cm allowing their application at high frequencies [5.16]. Firing at high temperatures provokes a partial dissociation by loss of oxygen in the bulk of the grains, accompanied by the change of ferric cations into the ferrous state, whilst cooling re-oxidizes their surfaces and renders them insulating. The ferrites, which are semiconductors, thus behave like hematite with valence induction by TiO_2 as described in the preceding section. The dispersion in their apparent a.c. resistivity and permittivity was described for the first time by KOOPS [5.8] for the ferrite $Ni_{0·4}Zn_{0·6}Fe_2O_4$, by FAIRWEATHER and FROST [5.17] for a mixed spinel $MgFe_2O_4/MgAl_2O_4$, and by VOLGER [5.18] for a mixed manganite $La_{0·9}Sr_{0·1}MnO_3$.

It may be expected that the existence of a surface layer can be disclosed by a study of the magnetic properties. PARKER [5.19], in a discussion of Volger's results, showed that in the surface region formed by oxidation the material is not spontaneously magnetized. This occurs because not too far below the Curie point, at which thermal agitation destroys the ferrimagnetism, the disorganization of the crystal lattice can attenuate the interactions between the A and B sub-lattices of the ferrite sufficiently so that it has a paramagnetic shell on the surface of each grain, and more especially at the surface of those grains situated on the surface of the sample. SUCHET [5.9] showed that it was possible to calculate the thickness of the insulating surface layer for the case of the nickel-zinc ferrite studied by Koops from the results given by the latter (Table 5.3). The values cor-

TABLE 5.3

Atmosphere during sintering	Method of cooling	Concentration of ferrous ions after sintering (%)	Thickness of surface layer (Å)
Air	Rapid	0·42	1·0
Oxygen	Rapid	0·38	5·4
Air	Slow	0·07	20
Oxygen	Slow	0·10	32

responding to rapid cooling indicated a chemisorption of oxygen, which was most clearly marked when the sintering took place in pure oxygen. In the case of slow cooling, the greatly increased thickness of the oxide layer indicates a mechanism of almost complete oxidation which would significantly decrease the concentration of ferrous ions. It may be suggested in this latter case that the surface layer acquires a structure analogous to that of γ-hematite (cubic), which has a relatively high stability when obtained from substituted magnetites:

$$(Fe^{3+})_t(Fe^{2+}Fe^{3+})_oO_4 + \tfrac{1}{4}O^2 \longrightarrow (Fe^{3+})_3O_{4.5}$$

Ferrimagnetism can evidently no longer subsist under these conditions.

In almost all magnetic materials one observes an ageing corresponding to a decrease of permeability with time which can, however, be annulled by submitting the material to a magnetic shock such as the action of a demagnetizing alternating field. Hence the name 'reversible ageing' (we shall employ here the term 'disaccommodation' or in brief 'the D.A.', used in Dutch publications). This phenomenon, described in detail by WEBB and FORD [5.20], has been explained for soft iron and for the silicon–iron alloys by SNOEK [5.11] in terms of the dissolved carbon and nitrogen. In the case of mixed manganese and zinc ferrites it may cause significant drifts as is shown in Fig. 5.14. The drift of permeability in twenty-four hours, with respect to its value measured one minute after demagnetization, is designated by D.A. in Fig. 5.15, which shows its variation as a function of temperature and of the atmosphere during firing for the $Mn_{0.6}\,Zn_{0.4}\,Fe_2O_4$ ferrites with molar concentrations of Fe_2O_3 varying from 50 to 54% (that is to say, containing a small quantity of magnetite Fe_3O_4). One sees that the large values of the D.A. coincide with concentrations of Fe_2O_3 of

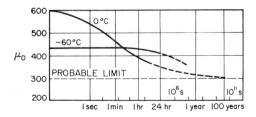

FIG. 5.14. Reversible ageing (D.A.) of Mn-Zn ferrite
(following SNOEK [5, 11])

52% and more, for which a significant surface oxide layer is formed during cooling. It decreases for high firing temperatures, which correspond to small porosity of the ceramic. The phenomenon of D.A. thus appears to be related to a rearrangement of the Bloch walls taking into account the discontinuities caused by the paramagnetic surface layers [5.9].

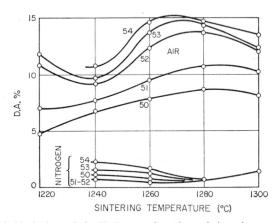

FIG. 5.15. Variation of the D.A. as a function of sintering temperature
(following SUCHET [5.9])

The elimination of this phenomenon, which is most prejudicial to the properties of the ferrites, is thus bound up with the suppression of the superficial oxidized layers on the grains of the ceramics. To do this it is necessary to have a moderate firing temperature so as not to give rise to a loss of oxygen, and a small degree of porosity in order to reduce re-oxidation by the atmosphere during cooling. The firing temperature and porosity vary in opposite senses, and these two conditions can only be satisfied simultaneously by using iron oxide powders with very fine grains such as the synthetic hematites (0·1 to 0·2 microns). The incorporation of copper in the ferrite also has a beneficial influence because, of the two cations Fe^{2+} and Cu^+ formed during the firing, Cu^+ has an ionization energy less than that of Fe^{2+} (20 eV instead of 31 eV for the free atoms) and thus protects the latter by being oxidized before it. For analogous reasons the incorporation of manganese or cobalt in a nickel ferrite increases its resistivity by diminishing the reduction of the ferric ions during firing, the interchanges Mn^{2+}—Mn^{3+} and Co^{2+}—Co^{3+} corresponding for the free atoms to an ionization energy of 34 eV as against 31 for Fe^{2+}—Fe^{3+} [5.21].

Chapter 6

PHYSICAL PROPERTIES AND THE CHEMICAL BOND

6.1 The Energy Gap and Electron Mobility

METALLIC crystals absorb electromagnetic radiation of almost all wave-lengths, because the electron-photon collisions simply have the effect of increasing the kinetic energy of the free electrons, transferring to them the energy $h\nu$ of the photon. On the other hand, non-metallic crystals contain very few free electrons, and a photon is only absorbed if it has an energy greater than the energy gap E_G which an electron requires to break free from a bonding orbital. Thus these crystals possess an **absorption edge** at $h\nu = E_G$, and we can say to a first approximation that they are transparent in the infra-red region, and opaque in the ultra-violet. Their behaviour in the visible region will depend upon the value of E_G. They will range from the transparency of diamond or of rocksalt (E_G in the region of 5 eV) to the almost metallic lustre of pyrites or germanium (E_G less than 1 eV) via the adamantine lustre of the numerous phosphides and sulphides which have intermediate values.

The energy gap (**énergie d'activation** or **largeur de bande interdite** in French publications) may be interpreted simply in terms of an absorption edge at a limiting frequency ν_f below which the creation of an electron-hole pair in the crystals by the photoelectric effect cannot occur. It is the energy which, transferred to a bonding electron, frees this electron leaving in its place a hole in the electronic distribution of the atom. The simplest case is that of the hydrogen molecule, where an electron which is bonding when its spin is opposed to that of the other electron in the ground state can be excited to an antibonding state, in which its spin is parallel. The energetic difference between the two states may be called the energy gap. Thus, for example, an electron in the p bonding states of silicon will pass to p antibonding states (cf. also Appendix). Planck's constant has a value $h = 4 \cdot 14 \times 10^{-15}$ eVs, thus an energy gap of one electronvolt corresponds to an absorption edge located at a wavelength of $1 \cdot 24\ \mu$, i.e. in the near infra-red. The absorption edges of silicon and germanium are in the same

96

region, situated respectively at 1·10 and 1·72 μ. On the other hand, that of zinc oxide is at 0·39 μ, at the other extreme of the visible spectrum.

The energy E_G plays a fundamental role in the sort of semiconductivity which was defined in Section 1.2, i.e. **intrinsic semiconductivity.**

The thermal energies of the electrons increase with increasing temperature, and the critical energy E_G is achieved by an ever increasing number of electrons as the temperature is raised. At high temperatures where the influence of the mechanisms of semiconductivity described in Chapter 2 is generally negligible and, in the absence of electrolytic conductivity, it can be shown that the electronic conductivity varies according to the expression:

$$\sigma = \sigma_o \exp\left(-E_G/kT\right)$$

whence the common practice of plotting log σ as a function of $1/T$.

In Chapter 2 we have already seen that near room temperatures the conductivity is determined principally by the numbers N or P of charge carriers (electrons or holes) arising from active point defects in the crystal and that it depends, moreover, on the **mobility** of these carriers:

$$\sigma = e(N\mu_n + P\mu_p)$$

The mobility μ of these carriers may be reduced by their interactions with the crystalline medium which gives scattering of the carriers (cf. [7], p. 255). One may distinguish **polar scattering,** caused for example, in ionic crystals by the presence of ions whose regular arrangement subjects a carrier moving in a straight line to periodic attractive and repulsive forces, and **non-polar scattering,** simply caused by the thermal vibrations of the atoms and the resulting fluctuation of potential at each point. In addition, the presence of local imperfections (vacancies, interstitials and impurities) gives rise to significant **defect scattering.**

The first two kinds of scattering are clearly related, since the ionic and covalent characteristics of a crystal cannot be totally separated. For both of them the increase in the amplitude of lattice vibrations when the temperature is increased, results in a decrease in the carrier mobility. Polar scattering is usually more important than non-polar scattering so that at a given temperature, the mobility of a carrier will often be much higher in a crystal having a measure of covalent character than in a purely ionic crystal. Finally, scattering by crystalline imperfections is well understood and semiconductor technology always strives towards more pure and more perfect crystals in order to reduce its influence. The gradual and regular increase as time passes in the quoted values for carrier mobility are themselves a measure of this progress.

The energy gap and carrier mobility together with the thermal conductivity, are the essential physical properties to be considered in the specification of semiconductivity in a crystal. Table 6.1 shows values collected by

TABLE 6.1

Semiconductor	E_G 0°K (eV)	E_G amb. (eV)	μ amb. (cm²/Vs)	k amb. (mW/cm deg.)
Ge	0·744	0·67	3800	700
Si	1·153	1·107	1300	1300
Te	0·33	—	1100	—
Se amorphous	—	1·86	—	—
C diamond	—	5·4	—	5700
Mg_2Si	0·77	—	406	—
Mg_2Ge	0·74	—	280	100
Mg_2Sn	0·33	0·21	318	100
ZnSb	0·56	—	10	14
CdSb	0·59	0·465	300	10
Mg_3Sb_2	0·82	—	19	—
Zn_3As_2 α	—	0·93	10	—
Cd_3As_2	—	0·13	1500	110
ZnO	—	3·2	180	6
ZnS β	—	3·54	—	—
ZnSe	2·80	2·58	100	—
ZnTe	—	2·26	—	—
CdO	—	2·5	120	7
CdS α	—	2·42	210	—
CdSe α	1·85	1·74	500	—
CdTe β	1·56	1·44	600	—
HgSe	—	0·3	5500	—
HgTe	—	0·15	22000	27
AlN	—	3·8	—	—
AlP	—	3·0	—	—
AlAs	—	2·16	—	—
AlSb	1·70	1·60	50	—
GaN	—	3·25	—	—
GaP	2·4	2·24	—	—
GaAs	1·53	1·35	6000	370
GaSb	0·813	—	4000	270
InP	1·41	1·27	4000	~500
InAs	0·43	0·360	30000	290
InSb	0·27	0·180	76000	150
SiC β	2·68	2·2	—	—
GeS	—	1·77	—	—
SnS	—	1·26	—	—
SnSe	—	0·88	—	—
PbS	—	0·38	550	8
PbSe	—	0·26	1020	17
PbTe	—	0·28	1620	22
As_2Te_3	—	1·0	170	25
Sb_2Se_3	1·35	1·2	15?	—
Sb_2Te_3	—	0·3	—	55
Bi_2S_3	—	1·3	200	—
Bi_2Se_3	—	0·35	600	24
Bi_2Te_3	0·17	0·15	1250	25

AIGRAIN and BALKANSKI [6.1]. Many authors have attempted to relate these values to parameters such as the interatomic distance, the bond energy, the electronegativity, the polarization, etc., with a view to explaining their variation from one crystal to another within particular series having analogous crystal structures or chemical composition. In 1951, IOFFE [6.2] showed that semiconductivity was not necessarily related to the presence of rigorous crystalline order and predicted the existence of vitreous and liquid semiconductors, which possessed only short range order. One may deduce from this that *the principal physical properties of a semiconductor may be derived as functions of the nature of the principal atoms present, the bond lengths separating them and their spatial arrangements.*

The physico-chemical parameters which one may consider using in order to specify a given arrangement of atoms, are unfortunately often still the subject of controversy, so that it seems essential to review the fundamental ideas. We shall review successively the ideas of ionic radius, bond energy, electronegativity and ionic character.

6.2 Ionic Radii and Covalent 'Radii'

Shortly after the publication by BRAGG [6.3] of the first rough values of atomic radii, it was recognized that these values depended in fact upon the nature of the atom, the structure of the crystal containing it and the sort of bond which it formed with its neighbours. The concept of radius is particularly justified for atomic ions, because of the spherical symmetry of their electrostatic fields. The values proposed by LANDÉ [6.4] and WASAST-JERNA [6.5] show that additivity of ionic radii holds for the alkali halides.

TABLE 6.2

			H^- 2.08	He	Li^+ 0.60	Be^{2+} 0.31	B^{3+} 0.20	C^{4+} 0.15	N^{5+} 0.11	O^{6+} 0.09	F^{7+} 0.07
C^{4-} 2.60	N^{3-} 1.71	O^{2-} 1.40	F^- 1.36	Ne	Na^+ 0.95	Mg^{2+} 0.65	Al^{3+} 0.50	Si^{4+} 0.41	P^{5+} 0.34	S^{6+} 0.29	Cl^{7+} 0.26
Si^{4-} 2.71	P^{3-} 2.12	S^{2-} 1.84	Cl^- 1.81	Ar	K^+ 1.33	Ca^{2+} 0.99	Sc^{3+} 0.81	Ti^{4+} 0.68	V^{5+} 0.59	Cr^{6+} 0.52	Mn^{7+} 0.46
					Cu^+ 0.96	Zn^{2+} 0.74	Ga^{3+} 0.62	Ge^{4+} 0.53	As^{5+} 0.47	Se^{6+} 0.42	Br^{7+} 0.39
Ge^{4-} 2.72	As^{3-} 2.22	Se^{2-} 1.98	Br^- 1.95	Kr	Rb^+ 1.48	Sr^{2+} 1.13	Y^{3+} 0.93	Zr^{4+} 0.80	Cb^{5+} 0.70	Mo^{6+} 0.62	
					Ag^+ 1.26	Cd^{2+} 0.97	In^{3+} 0.81	Sn^{4+} 0.71	Sb^{5+} 0.62	Te^{6+} 0.56	I^{7+} 0.50
Sn^{4-} 2.94	Sb^{3-} 2.45	Te^{2-} 2.21	I^- 2.16	Xe	Cs^+ 1.69	Ba^{2+} 1.35	La^{3+} 1.15	Ce^{4+} 1.01			
					Au^+ 1.37	Hg^{2+} 1.10	Tl^{3+} 0.95	Pb^{4+} 0.84	Bi^{5+} 0.74		

Table 6.3

I_A	I_B	$II_{A/B}$	III_B	IV_B	V_B	VI_B	VII_B
$Li_{IV} = 1·35$		$Be_{IV} = 1·06$		$C_{IV} = 0·77$	$N_{IV} = 0·70$		
$Na_{IV} = 1·70$		$Mg_{IV} = 1·40$	$Al_{IV} = 1·26$	$Si_{IV} = 1·17$	$P_{IV} = 1·10$	$S_{IV} = 1·04$	
				$Si_{VIII} = 1·37$	$P_{VIII} = 1·25$	$S_{VIII} = 1·12$	
$K_{IV} = 2·05$	$Cu_{IV} = 1·35$	$Zn_{IV} = 1·31$	$Ga_{IV} = 1·26$	$Ge_{IV} = 1·22$	$As_{IV} = 1·18$	$Se_{IV} = 1·14$	
				$Ge_{VIII} = 1·36$	$As_{VIII} = 1·30$	$Se_{VIII} = 1·25$	
$Rb_{IV} = 2·25$	$Ag_{IV} = 1·53$	$Cd_{IV} = 1·48$	$In_{IV} = 1·44$	$Sn_{IV} = 1·40$	$Sb_{IV} = 1·36$	$Te_{IV} = 1·32$	$I_{IV} = 1·28$
				$Sn_{VIII} = 1·53$	$Sb_{VIII} = 1·50$	$Te_{VIII} = 1·47$	$I_{VIII} = 1·43$
$Cs_{IV} = 2·55$	$Au_{IV} = 1·50$	$Hg_{IV} = 1·48$	$Tl_{IV} = 1·47$	$Pb_{IV} = 1·46$	$Bi_{IV} = 1·46$		
				$Pb_{VIII} = 1·56$	$Bi_{VIII} = 1·56$		

M_{IV} tetrahedral radius (apparent co-ordination 4)
M_{VIII} cubic radius (apparent co-ordination 8)

The radii of the halogen anions were established by supposing that they were in contact in the lithium halides. The first complete table was established by GOLDSCHMIDT [6.6], (cf. also [3]); some values for the transition metals have been given already in Table 5.2. PAULING [6.7] justified the calculation of these radii by theoretical considerations and presented a series of modified radii whose values appear in Table 6.2. He also presented a table of covalent tetrahedral radii for the blende structure. It is well understood that the term 'radius' cannot be taken in its literal sense when the compound has an appreciable covalent character, because the directional nature of the covalent bond excludes spherical symmetry. In these circumstances it is better to speak of the **atomic contribution to the bond length.**

Table 6.3 shows the tetrahedral radii of the atoms (Å) for which non-resonant iono-covalent sp^3 orbital hybrid bonds occur, and gives, in addition, the cubic radii (with resonance). We saw previously (Section 3.5) that the $C1$ structure and the partial lattice of the DO_3 structure both show co-ordinations of 8 for the Zintl atom and 4 for the metallic atom. If one takes Pauling's tetrahedral radius for the latter, the bond lengths in the $II_2 IV$ binary compounds such as Mg_2Sn allow one to calculate the cubic radii for the Column IV elements. One can suppose that the radii of lead and bismuth are equal for co-ordination 8, as they are for co-ordination 4, since they use the same kind of orbital. The partial lattices $[I_2 V]^-$ can thus be used for Li_{IV} and Sb_{VIII}, and the $I_2 VI$ binary compounds then complete the tetrahedral radii for the alkalis and give the cubic radii for the Group VI elements. The radii P_{VIII} and As_{VIII} are obtained by interpolation, and one can verify from the interatomic distances in the $(\square II_3) V_2$ binary compounds such as Zn_3P_2 that the perturbations caused by the presence of a vacancy in the $C1$ structure is small (cf. SUCHET [6.8]).

Table 6.4 gives the trigonal pyramidal and octahedral radii (Å) of the

TABLE 6.4

III_B	IV_B	V_B	VI_B	VII_B
		$P_{III} = 1\cdot08$	$S_{III} = 1\cdot18$	
			$S_{VI} = 1\cdot30$	
	$Ge_{III} = 1\cdot37$	$As_{III} = 1\cdot25$	$Se_{III} = 1\cdot20$	
	$Ge_{VI} = 1\cdot46$	$As_{VI} = 1\cdot42$	$Se_{VI} = 1\cdot41$	
	$Sn_{III} = 1\cdot47$	$Sb_{III} = 1\cdot43$	$Te_{III} = 1\cdot40$	$I_{III} = 1\cdot36$
	$Sn_{VI} = 1\cdot63$	$Sb_{VI} = 1\cdot56$	$Te_{VI} = 1\cdot51$	$I_{VI} = 1\cdot47$
	$Pb_{III} = 1\cdot56$	$Bi_{III} = 1\cdot55$		
$Tl_{VI} = 1\cdot81$	$Pb_{VI} = 1\cdot66$	$Bi_{VI} = 1\cdot64$		

M_{III} trigonal radius   (apparent co-ordination 3)
M_{VI} octahedral radius (apparent co-ordination 6)

atoms for which iono-covalent bonds with pure p^3 orbitals (with or without resonance) can occur. The trigonal radii of the elements of Column V are no more than the half-distances within the double atomic layer of the *A1* structure, whilst the averages of these distances and the distances separating the atoms of two successive double layers in the metallic forms give an idea of the octahedral radii which these elements would have in a hypothetical structure with co-ordination 6. The regular decrease of the radii as a function of atomic number allows one to give a figure for Se_{VI} with respect to As_{VI}, and the bond lengths in the IV VI binary compounds of the *B1* structure provide the evidence to complete the octahedral radii for the Group IV and VI elements. The ($\square$ IV) VII_2 binary compounds with *C6* structure give the I_{VI} radius and by supposing that the atoms of thallium touch in the case of $[Tl_{VI}]^{2-}Mg^{2+}$ (*B2* structure), one obtains a value for Tl_{VI}.

Table 6.5 gives the plane trigonal radii (Å) for the atoms in which iono-covalent bonds with non-resonant sp^2 orbital hybrids occur. These radii

TABLE 6.5

I_A	III_B	IV_B	V_B
$Li_{III} = 1·54$ $Na_{III} = 1·94$ $K_{III} = 2·36$ $Rb_{III} = 2·50$	$B_{III} = 0·88$	$C_{III} = 0·71$	$N_{III} = 0·57$ $P_{III} = 0·91$ $As_{III} = 0·98$ $Sb_{III} = 1·13$ $Bi_{III} = 1·21$

M_{III}　trigonal plane radius (apparent co-ordination 3)

are obtained by comparing the increases Δr of the trigonal and tetrahedral radii for Columns I and V of the periodic classification in passing from one element to the next, and by supposing that the radii themselves are in the same ratio. One finds on average, for the light elements, that $\Delta r_{III}/\Delta r_{IV} = 1·14$ for the alkalis, and 0·83 for the elements of Column V. The radii obtained agree well with those for carbon (graphite) and for boron, as well as with that of nitrogen calculated from BN. One can finally complete this group with the aid of the following radii:

$$S_{II} = 1·05,\ Se_{II} = 1·16,\ Te_{II} = 1·43,\ Po_{II} = 1·67,\ I_{II} = 1·40,\ I_I = 1·33.$$

A comparison of the ionic radii with the covalent radii (or, more exactly, iono-covalent) which we propose is of interest in some cases. Thus one sees that the Tl–I distance in α TlI is intermediate between $Tl_{VI} + I_{VI}$ and $Tl^+ + I^-$, and that the V–VI^{2-} distances in the compensated lattice

[V VI]$_2^+$ VI^{2-} are similarly intermediate between V$_{III}$ + VI^{2-} and V^{3+} + VI^{2-}, (Sb^{3+} $\simeq$ 0·85 and Bi^{3+} $\simeq$ 1·0, cf. later Fig. 6.1). We conclude from this that in either case the bond is almost completely ionic, and this confirms both the large value of λ_0 = 0·67 found for αTlI and the application of the idea of a compensated lattice to Bi$_2$Te$_3$. We must emphasize that all the radii calculated above are approximate to within one or two per cent, the least well defined being those for the elements prone to form compounds of a strongly ionic nature, such as the alkalis, alkaline-earths and halides. Finally, let us note that the average increase

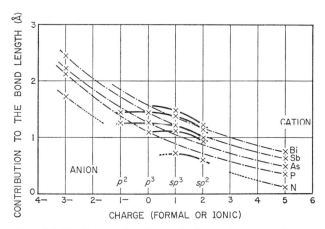

FIG. 6.1. Variation of radius with charge, formal or ionic
(following SUCHET [6.9])

in radii caused by a mono-electronic bond (resonance) is of the order of 10% in the case of pure p orbitals as well as in that of s-p orbital hybrids.

It has been shown that the ionic radii depend on the ionic charges attached to the symbols for the crystal where the ionic character predominates; thus the covalent radii will depend on the formal charges which one is led to attribute to them in a covalent notation [6.9]. Figure 6.1 compares these variations for elements of Group V. The neutral state of the atom was taken as that corresponding to trigonal pyramidal bonds for the elements.

6.3 Electronegativity and Ionic Character

Experimental values for single bond energies in diatomic molecules are obtained by measuring the energy required for dissociation, by thermochemical or spectroscopic methods. In the case of a polyatomic molecule, the thermochemical method gives the total dissociation energy of the atoms, whence one may extract the mean value of the energy for a single bond. Table 6.6 gives, following PAULING [6.7], some bond energies (in kilocalories per mole) for two identical atoms, that is $2Q/c$ if Q is the bond energy per atom and c the number of single bonds which each of them forms with similar neighbours.

TABLE 6.6

Bond	Bond energy	Bond	Bond energy	Bond	Bond energy
H–H	104·2	P–P	51·3	Se–Se	44
C–C	83·1	As–As	32·1	Te–Te	33
Si–Si	42·2	Sb–Sb	30·2	F–F	36·6
Ge–Ge	37·6	Bi–Bi	25	Cl–Cl	58
Sn–Sn	34·2	O–O	33·2	Br–Br	46·1
N–N	38·4	S–S	50·9	I–I	36·1

The concept of electronegativity was introduced by PAULING [6.10] in 1932. It is concerned with atoms in molecules or crystals, and not with isolated atoms. It is the 'attractive power of an atom for electrons'. The difference in electronegativity between two atoms M and X forming a molecule MX thus constitutes some measure of the electron transfer produced by the establishment of an iono-covalent bond. Pauling noted that the M–X bond energy was usually greater than the arithmetic mean of the bond energies M–M and X–X, and that the relative displacement δ appeared to increase with increasing difference of electronegativity Δx_1 between M and X as otherwise roughly assessed. He put forward the formula:

$$\Delta x_1 = 0·208\delta^{\frac{1}{2}}$$
$$\delta = Q(\text{M–X}) - \tfrac{1}{2}[Q(\text{M–M}) + Q(\text{X–X})]$$

as a definition of electronegativity.

The consistency between this formula and experiment is not very good, and it only constitutes a rough approximation, apart from the alkali iodides and hydracids. The agreement is better among the MX_n compounds where the bond energy considered is $1/n$th of the dissociation energy of the molecule. In all, there are values for thirty-three elements, taking an arbitrary value of 2·1 for hydrogen; they appear in Fig. 6.2, and are known as Pauling's **electronegativities.** Other values have subsequently been calculated by HAISSINSKY [6.11] using the same thermochemical method.

Another definition of electronegativity (under the name electro-affinity) was proposed by MULLIKEN [6.12] in 1934 as the mean of the ionization potential I and the electron affinity A of an atom:

$$\Delta x_2 = \tfrac{1}{2}(I + A)$$

The ionization potential may be deduced from spectroscopic observations, but there is a shortage of information on the electron affinities. The important novelty that this definition presents with respect to Pauling's formula is that it depends on the valence state of the atom. Taking into consideration the approximate nature of the determinations, Mulliken's scheme nevertheless more or less follows that of Pauling, with $\Delta x_2 \simeq \Delta x_1/3\cdot15$.

Formulae for electronegativity have been proposed by GORDY [6.13], [6.14] from the attractive force constant for the atoms M and X, their bond length, the number of valence electrons η and the covalent radius r calculated from diatomic molecules (univalent radius). Other formulae have been proposed by other authors. All the values of x obtained from these different formulae agree more or less, as shown in the excellent critical

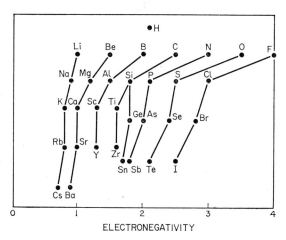

ELECTRONEGATIVITY

FIG. 6.2. Table of electronegativities (following PAULING [6.7])

studies made by PRITCHARD and SKINNER [6.15] and rather later by GORDY and THOMAS [6.16]. The latter authors' final list of probable values, calculated independently, is virtually identical, but more complete (Fig. 6.3).

The concept of electronegativity has been applied by PAULING (6.7) to the estimation of the percentage ionic character of a bond. He first supposed that the ionic character of the halogen acids could be deduced from their dipole moment. Thus, the observed moment for HCl is equal to 17% of the moment which would be produced by two point charges placed at the respective nuclei, and those of HBr and HI are 11% and 5% respectively. The ionic character is thus linked with the difference in electronegativity by the empirical formula:

$$\text{ionic character (\%)} = 100\ \{1 - \exp\left[-(\Delta x)^2/4\right]\}$$

This formula was shown to be incorrect following the measurement of the

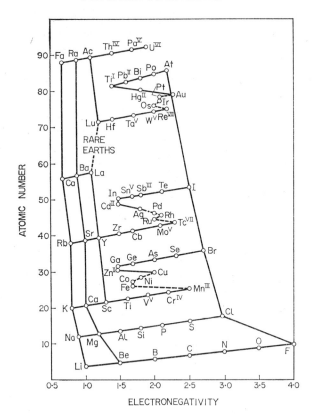

FIG. 6.3. Table of electronegativities (following GORDY and THOMAS [6.16])

dipole moment of HF by HANNAY and SMYTH [6.17]. The idea of a simple correspondence between the dipole moment and ionic character has also been questioned by ROBINSON [6.18]. The percentage ionic characters given by Pauling must hence be treated with the greatest care. In any case, we have seen that apart from the ionicity, linked rightly or wrongly to the dipole moment, there is also an additional ionicity related to the value c of the covalent co-ordination (Section 2.5). However, in the case of the halogen acid envisaged above, $c = 1$, and this second ionicity is zero. In effect one finds $c(1 - \lambda_0) = c(1 + \lambda_0) = 1$ whence $\lambda_0 = 0$. The numbers 0·17–0·11–0·05 would thus measure the difference $\lambda - \lambda_0 = q/c$, q here being the effective charge, *if the latter could be rigorously related to the measured dipole moment*, which is not very likely.

6.4 Attempts to Calculate the Energy Gap

For the semiconducting elements of Column IV of the periodic classification GOODMAN [6.19] has given a graph showing $E_G^{1/2}$ (at 300°K) as a function of $10/d^2$, where d is the bond length. It shows that Si, Ge and Sn (grey) fall virtually on a straight line. For the binary III–V compounds whose bond lengths are known this graph gives values of E_G which are always smaller than the energy gap, and which one can hence consider as the covalent contribution E_1 to the energy gap. Thus the difference will be the ionic contribution E_2:

$$E_G = E_1 + E_2$$

This work has been extended by the author [6.8] to the series of semi-conducting elements from Columns V (P, As, Sb) and VI (S, Se, Te) crystallizing in the A7 and A8 structures respectively. If instead of the bond length d one substitutes half its value r, considered as a characteristic radius for the atom, one can hope to calculate the E_1 contribution for compounds for which the distances d are unknown. This has been done by the author who used the covalent radii of Section 6.2, and obtained the following empirical relationships:

$$s\text{-}p \text{ orbital hybrids: } E_1^{1/2} = (1/r + 1/r')^2 - \alpha$$

$$\text{pure } p \text{ orbitals: }\quad E_1^{1/2} = (1/r + 1/r')^{3/2} - \alpha$$

with $\alpha = 1\cdot 87$ (sp^3 orbital), $1\cdot 31$ (p^3 orbitals), $1\cdot 04$ (p^2 orbitals) and $0\cdot 71$ (p orbitals).

It was noted originally that the energy gaps of compounds in an iso-electronic series increased with the ionic character defined according to Pauling. In particular those of the III–V compounds are very much higher than those of the isoelectronic Group IV elements (for example, GaAs and Ge). WELKER [6.20] explained this fact as arising from an increase in the bond energy due to a resonance between the covalent and ionic contributions. However, better knowledge of these compounds subsequently showed that the energy gap decreased in a series such as AlSb–GaAs–InP or GaSb–InAs although the ionic character increases (Table 6.7, following [6.21]). Thus it is clear that the electronegativity of the constituent atoms is not the only factor to intervene, and many authors have also introduced the sum of the atomic numbers, or the total number of electrons $(Z + Z')$ whose role could be linked with the phenomenon of polarization (cf. following section). The simplest expression for the contribution E_2 is due to BUBE [7], who, moreover, identifies it with the energy gap, ignoring the covalent contribution. It can be expressed:

$$E_2 = C\,(\eta' - \eta)/(Z + Z')$$

where η and η' represent the number of valence electrons of the cation and

TABLE 6.7

ionic character
———————→

AlSb	GaAs	InP
1·70	1·53	1·41

GaSb	InAs
0·81	0·43

←———————
energy gap

anion respectively, and thus constitute a simplified table of electronegativity. C is a constant for which the value forty-three is proposed. There is
some justification for dividing this constant by two in the case of single
electron bonds. Another expression which is due to PEARSON [6.22] and is
applicable in blende structures, contains the parameter $\bar{n}$, the average
principal quantum number, which introduces the total number of electrons
in the form $(Z + Z')^{\frac{1}{2}}$ and the electronegativities as given by GORDY
and THOMAS [6.16]. It is written:

$$E_2 = c.\Delta x.\exp b$$

where b and c are functions of $\bar{n}$, and E_1 is equated with the energy gap
for the Column IV isoelectronic element (Table 6.8). The use of the
parameter $\bar{n}$ is justified by the interest in obtaining a two-dimensional representation of the function in terms of $\bar{n}$ and Δx, where there are well-
defined regions corresponding to the type of structure in which the various
compounds crystallize, [6.23]. Other calculations based on thermodynamic
considerations have been made by ORMONT [6.24].

The author has shown that the table of electronegativities given by
Pauling cannot be utilized on such a basis for the calculation of E_2 [6.8].
Table 6.9 gives the value of E_2, obtained by subtracting E_1 from the ex-
perimental energy gap, for pairs of isoelectronic binary compounds, in

TABLE 6.8

$\bar{n}$	E_1	c	b
3	1·21	2·97	1
4	0·75	2·19	1·5
5	0·08	6·4	3

TABLE 6.9

Compound	E_G experimental (room temp.)	E_1 calculated	$E_2 = E_G - E_1$
AlAs	2·16	0·67	1·49
GaP	2·24	1·05	1·19
GaSb	0·70	0·21	0·49
InAs	0·36	0·25	0·11
ZnTe	2·26	0·19	2·07
CdSe	1·74	0·29	1·45

such a way as to eliminate the possible influence of the sum $(Z + Z')$. One finds that this contribution, and as a consequence the difference of electronegativities Δx between the constituent atoms, is always much larger when the heavy atom is one of the Zintl atoms. This results in a certain sloping of the lines joining the elements of the same column (Fig. 6.4), and the segments have an opposite slope in Pauling's well-known table of electronegativities (Fig. 6.2). Therefore, an empirical expression containing $\log (Z + Z')$ is proposed, which gives fairly good agreement with the experimental results. Except for the III–V compounds E_1 is negligible compared with E_2.

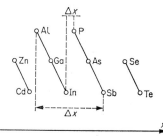

FIG. 6.4. Relative electronegativities of the Group III and Group V elements

Recently, MANCA [6.25] has attempted to calculate the energy of a single bond for different semiconductors crystallizing in the diamond and blende structures by means of the following formulae due to Pauling:

$$E_s = (E_{sM} . E_{sX})^{\frac{1}{2}} + \Delta x^2$$

E_{sM} and E_{sX} are the energies for a single bond for the elements M and X and the values of Δx are those of Gordy and Thomas. Thus one obtains a linear relationship:

$$E_G = \alpha(E_s - \beta)$$

where the parameters α and β are constants for each series of compounds such as the III V's, or II VI's.

6.5. Attempts to Calculate the Electron Mobility

It should be possible to relate the value of the maximum mobility (for an ideal crystal) to the importance of its ionic character. It is this idea which led GOODMAN [6.19] to take as a parameter the ionic contribution to the energy gap E_2, or more exactly the quantity $(d^3E_2)^{\frac{1}{2}}$ considered as an evaluation of the crystalline dipole where $(dE_2)^{\frac{1}{2}}$ would represent the effective charge (Fig. 6.5 according to Goodman). One finds that the mobility passes through a maximum for InSb in the blende structure, but this relationship leads to confusion, as we shall see later, by suggesting that the existence of a large mobility is related to the presence of a weak ionic character in the bond.

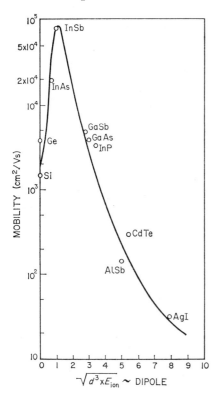

FIG. 6.5. Relationship between the mobility and crystalline dipole (following GOODMAN [7.2])

We have already referred to the phenomenon of polarization in Section 1.2; the forces acting between two ions can no longer be considered as coulombic forces when the two ions are sufficiently close, and when one or both of them possesses a large number of electrons. If the ions carry charges $+n$ and $-n$ respectively, at a distance l they give rise to potentials $+n/l$ and $-n/l$ and hence to electric fields of $-n/l^2$ and $+n/l^2$. The electrons themselves are subject to forces $+ne/l^2$ and $-ne/l^2$, and their mean position will be displaced with respect to that of the nucleus and an **electric dipole** is formed. If we suppose the two ions to be in contact and consider only the polarization of the anion, we see that the outer electrons of the latter, along the line of the nuclei, will find themselves subject to the cationic potential $+n/r$, r being the radius of the cation. The ratios n/r for the principal cations (in units of electron charge and Ångströms) have been grouped in Table 1.4, and we observed that there were no semiconducting elements having ratios less than 7, whilst for higher ratios all the elements possessed semiconducting forms. If two atoms M and X are at distance d and if the anion forms a dipole X_1X_2 with charges

$-(n + \Delta n)$ and $-(n - \Delta n)$ at distance δ, the **dipole moment**, $\Delta n.\delta$, is proportional to the field to which it is subjected. Thus the polarizability, α = moment/field, is a characteristic of the atom or ion and can be determined from measurements of refractive index (cf. BÖTTCHER [6.26] and [3]). Figure 6.6 shows that for homologous ions this polarizability is an approximately linear function of the number of electrons, if the light atoms or ions for which Z is less than 10 are disregarded.

The intervention of polarization has been proposed by FOLBERTH [6.28] in order to explain the differences of energy gap and mobility in the III–V binary compounds. Atoms forming a purely covalent lattice (such as those

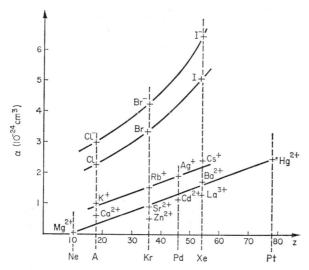

FIG. 6.6. Relationship between the polarizability and the number of electrons (following SUCHET [6.27])

of Si and Ge) in effect do not carry any charge, but it becomes necessary to take the latter into consideration immediately when one passes to a compound MX. If we consider a one-dimensional model of the crystal lattice, the passage from germanium to an isoelectronic III–V compound results in the modulation of the periodic potential function by a function with twice the wavelength but with an amplitude smaller than that of the fundamental. This modulation gives rise to a periodic function displaying alternate minima of different amplitude, and the ratio of amplitudes of the two synthesizing functions, or **degree of modulation** ε, thus gives a measure of the relative difference of the potential wells. If the amplitude of the fundamental is taken as unity, ε then represents the amplitude of the modulating wave (Fig. 6.7). Starting from the hypothesis of a unit MX made up of two completely ionized atoms M^{n+} and X^{n-}, we see that the

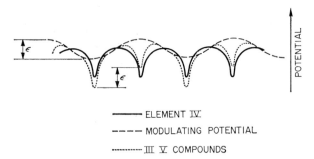

     —————— ELEMENT IV

     — — — — MODULATING POTENTIAL

     ·········· III V COMPOUNDS

FIG. 6.7. One-dimensional representation of the crystalline potential

polarization of the ions tends to reduce the charge n and that, if it is sufficiently important, one could in fact obtain a dipole $M^{(-)}X^{(+)}$; thus the degree of modulation changes sign passing through the value 0. This zero value would be achieved virtually, according to SLATER and KOSTER [6.29], in the case of InSb. After proposing a semi-empirical evaluation of the 'relative polarization', $J = f.(Z_{III} + V_V)^{3/2}$, Folberth classified the degree of modulation for the principal III–V compounds according to Fig. 6.8.

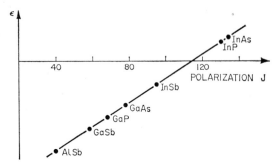

FIG. 6.8.   Degree of modulation for the III–V compounds
(following FOLBERTH [6.28])

We saw in Section 3.4 that the sign of the dipole in AlSb and GaSb were in good agreement with this classification, but the position of the other compounds is open to discussion. The hypotheses made for the evaluation of the quantity f are, moreover, very uncertain, as is the expression for J on which the degree of modulation depends. In fact, the attempts made by Goodman and Folberth both meet with the difficulty of calculating with sufficient precision the effective charge carried by the atoms of the crystal.

     Finally, let us mention the correlations which have been obtained with the heat of formation Q. RUPPEL et al. [6.30] found that log E_G was a very roughly linear function of Q for thirty-five elemental or compound semi-conductors. ZHUZE [6.31], on the other hand, indicated the existence of an equally good linear relationship for mobility:

$$\log \mu = -C \times \log Q$$

where the constant C takes different values for the blende and rocksalt structures.

Chapter 7

THE CRYSTALLOCHEMICAL MODEL

7.1 New Concept of the Iono-covalent Bond

We shall reconsider in a more fundamental way the concepts outlined in Section 2.5 and show more fully their importance in the study of compound semiconductors. All non-metallic inter-atomic bonds will be regarded as the super-position of a purely covalent and a purely ionic electronic distribution. The extreme distributions are shown schematically in Fig. 7.1.

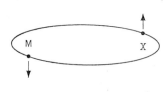

Our aim is to obtain a very general representation for the phenomenon of bonding. Let us consider a single M–X bond, in isolation from the other bonds which each of the atoms M and X may form. Suppose ϕ_M and ϕ_X are the atomic orbital wavefunctions which represent the states of the electrons in these two atoms when separated by infinity. We shall make the following assumptions:

FIG. 7.1. Covalent and ionic electron distributions

(1) ϕ_M and ϕ_X are orthogonal wavefunctions.

(2) A bonding orbital can be formed from the product of ϕ_M and ϕ_X.

(3) The electrons 1 and 2 of each shared pair, although indistinguishable in a purely covalent distribution (as pointed out by HEITLER and LONDON for the hydrogen molecule), do not play here the same role, since M and X are not identical.

(4) The atom X always plays the role of anion in the ionic distribution.

Thus the wavefunction for the system may be written [7.1]:

$$\psi = a\psi_{cov} + b\psi_{ion} = a\phi_M(1)\phi_X(2) + b\phi_X(1)\phi_X(2)$$
$$= [a\phi_M(1) + b\phi_X(1)].[\phi_X(2)]$$

114

The c shared bonding pairs formed by an atom with its near neighbours make up the $2c$ valence electrons participating in the bonds. We shall suppose that the state of half of them is described by the first bracket in the expression above (nomadic electrons as in Section 2.5) and that of the other half by the second bracket (sedentary electrons). Figure 2.15 illustrates this concept.

The number of bonding electrons whose state is represented by the orbital ϕ_M may be written $(1 - \lambda)$ per bond, that is $c(1 - \lambda)$ in all (nomadic electrons); whilst the number of those whose state is represented by ϕ_X is then λ (nomadic electrons) $+ 1$ per bond (sedentary electrons), that is $c(1 + \lambda)$ in all. More simply we can say that the bonding electrons are distributed as $c(1 - \lambda)$ on the atom M, $c(1 + \lambda)$ on the atom X in an extended crystal MX. We can also say that $(1 - \lambda)$ and λ are the respective **probabilities** of the covalent and ionic electron distributions symbolized in Fig. 7.1.

In order to evaluate these probabilities we shall proceed in two distinct steps [7.1]. Let us first suppose that we have constructed an array of **neutral** atoms having the same co-ordination as in the real crystal. One can imagine this by considering the crystal to be expanded so that inter-atomic distances are large and each atom may be considered as isolated. The number of bonding electrons that these atoms possess is known. The atom M is completely denuded of these electrons in the ionic scheme; the number of bonding electrons that it possesses is thus equal to the number which are transferred to the atom X in this scheme, i.e. n. As there are a total of $2c$ bonding electrons, $2c - n$ of them remains with atom X. Let us equate this distribution, for a certain value of the parameter λ_0 with the previous distribution:

$$n = c(1 - \lambda_0) \text{ on atom M}$$
$$2c - n = c(1 + \lambda_0) \text{ on atom X}$$

these two equations are satisfied for the same value:

$$\lambda_0 = (1 - n/c)$$

The values so obtained are presented in Table 2.1; λ_0 only depends on the position of the atoms M and X in the periodic classification and on the type of bond (tetrahedral, trigonal . . .). Thus it gives, for example, the same result for all the III V compounds. We have called λ_0 the **atomic ionicity.** Let us note that the simplified table of the electronegativities to which we referred in Section 6.4 in regard to Bube's formula is nothing more for the blende structure than

$$\eta' - \eta = c\lambda_0$$

Now let us consider the real crystal. We obtain it from the dilated crystal above by bringing the atoms closer to one another. Iono-covalent bonds are established between them and these are accompanied by a transfer of electrons due to the mutual polarization of the electron clouds. We shall designate by q the number of electrons thus transferred to an atom X by the c atoms M which surround it, or by q' the number of electrons transferred to an M atom by the c atoms X which surround it.* It is clear that the fictitious charges m and n introduced in Section 2.5 give limits for these numbers

$$q \leqslant n \quad \text{if} \quad q > 0 \quad \text{(transfer from M to X)}$$

$$|q| \leqslant m \quad \text{if} \quad q < 0 \quad \text{(transfer from X to M)}$$

We shall call q and q' the **effective charges** carried by the atoms M and X, in contrast to the **fictitious charges** m and n. The number of bonding electrons associated with atom X in the dilated crystal has been found to be $c(1 + \lambda_0)$. It is now augmented by a quantity q:

$$c(1 + \lambda) = c(1 + \lambda_0) + q$$

This gives a relationship for the definition and calculation of the probability λ, or the **crystalline ionicity** [7.2]:

$$\lambda = \lambda_0 + q/c$$

λ is obtained by adding to the atomic ionicity λ_0 a correction for **polarity** which is nothing more than the displaced charge per bond (q/c).

The author has proposed the following empirical formulae for the evaluation of the effective charges [7.3]:

cation: $q = n[1 - 0.01185(Z/r' + Z'/r)]$
anion: $q' = -n'[1 - 0.01185(Z/r' + Z'/r)]$

where Z and r are the total number of electrons and the ionic radii (following Pauling) of the atoms present. Primed values refer to the atom occupying the anion sites. Table 7.1 gives the values of Z, Z', $1/r$ and $1/r'$ $(\text{Å})^{-1}$ for the principal elements. In the case of ternary compounds such as ABX_2 where only the X atom occupies the anion sites and where no bonds are formed between the A and B atoms, one supposes that the A–X and B–X bonds are identical to those for binary compounds which crystallize to give structures of the same co-ordination, and one defines the average parameters λ_0, q' and λ with respect to the atom X. Thus for $AgInTe_2$, which crystallizes in the *E1* structure (chalcopyrite):

Ag–Te	$\lambda_0 = 0.75,$	$q = +0.24,$	$q' = -0.24,$	$\lambda = 0.81$
In–Te	0.25	-0.11	$+0.11$	0.22
$AgInTe_2$ (average)	0.50		-0.07	0.52

* This is a 'chemical' effective charge (see SUCHET, *C. R. Acad. Sci. Paris* **258**, 2305 (1964)).

TABLE 7.1

Z'	$1/r'$					$1/r$				Z
						Li^+ 1·67	Be^{2+} 3·22	B^{3+} 5·0	C^{4+} 6·67	2
10	C^{4-} 0·385	N^{3-} 0·585	O^{2-} 0·715	F^- 0·736	Ne	Na^+ 1·053	Mg^{2+} 1·539	Al^{3+} 2·0	Si^{4+} 2·44	10
									P^{3+} 1·924	12
18	Si^{4-} 0·369	P^{3-} 0·472	S^{2-} 0·543	Cl^- 0·553	Ar	K^+ 0·753	Ca^{2+} 1·01			18
					Ni	Cu^+ 1·043	Zn^{2+} 1·352	Ga^{3+} 1·613	Ge^{4+} 1·888	28
									As^{3+} 1·390	30
36	Ge^{4-} 0·368	As^{3-} 0·451	Se^{2-} 0·505	Br^- 0·513	Kr	Rb^+ 0·677	Sr^{2+} 0·885			36
					Pd	Ag^+ 0·794	Cd^{2+} 1·032	In^{3+} 1·235	Sn^{4+} 1·408	46
									Sb^{3+} 1·137	48
54	Sn^{4-} 0·340	Sb^{3-} 0·408	Te^{2-} 0·453	I^- 0·463	Xe	Cs^+ 0·592	Ba^{2+} 0·742			54
					Pt	Au^+ 0·730	Hg^{2+} 0·910	Tl^{3+} 1·054	Pb^{4+} 1·190	78
							Tl^+ 0·67	Pb^{2+} 0·76	Bi^{3+} 1·0	80
86	Pb^{4-} 0·337	Bi^{3-} 0·402			Rn					

Similarly in the case of vacancy lattices we should consider the vacancy as an atom of zero valence forming a purely ionic bond. Thus, for $\square In_2Te_3$, which crystallizes in the blende structure:

		$\lambda_0 = 1$,	$q = 0$,	$q' = 0$,	$\lambda = 1$
$\square$–Te		0·25	−0·11	+0·11	0·14
In–Te					
In_2Te_3 (average)		0·50		+0·07	0·43

7.2 Polarities and Ionicities of the Principal Semiconductors

Tables 7.2 (two electron tetrahedral bonds), 7.3 (ditto, single electron) and 7.4 (trigonal bonds, two and one electron) give a concise list of binary compounds of simple formulae as well as the corresponding values of c, λ_0, q and q'. λ has been given to two significant figures since correlation

C P S—I

TABLE 7.2

$(c = 4)$

IV IV ($\lambda_0 = 0$)		II VI ($\lambda_0 = 0.50$)	
$Si^{+2.7}C^{-2.7}$	$\lambda = 0.66$	$Mg^{-0.1}Te^{+0.1}$	$\lambda = 0.48$
		$Zn^{+1.2}O^{-1.2}$	0.80
III V ($\lambda_0 = 0.25$)		$Zn^{+1.1}S^{-1.1}$	0.77
$B^{+1.2}N^{-1.2}$	$\lambda = 0.54$	$Zn^{+0.5}Se^{-0.5}$	0.63
$Al^{+2.1}N^{-2.1}$	0.77	$Zn^{0}Te^{0}$	0.50
$Al^{+1.5}P^{-1.5}$	0.64	$Cd^{+1}S^{-1}$	0.74
$Al^{+0.3}As^{-0.3}$	0.32	$Cd^{+0.6}Se^{-0.6}$	0.64
$Al^{-1}Sb^{+1}$	0.01	$Cd^{+0.2}Te^{-0.2}$	0.54
$(Al^{-3.2}Bi^{+3.2}$	-0.56 metal)	$Hg^{+0.3}Se^{-0.3}$	0.57
$Ga^{+1.8}N^{-1.8}$	0.71	$Hg^{0}Te^{0}$	0.50
$Ga^{+1.5}P^{-1.5}$	0.62		
$Ga^{+0.5}As^{-0.5}$	0.37		
$Ga^{-0.5}Sb^{+0.5}$	0.13	**I VII ($\lambda_0 = 0.75$)**	
$(Ga^{-2.3}Bi^{+2.3}$	-0.33 metal)	$Cu^{+0.6}Cl^{-0.6}$	$\lambda = 0.90$
$In^{+1.6}N^{-1.6}$	0.65	$Cu^{+0.4}Br^{-0.4}$	0.85
$In^{+1.4}P^{-1.4}$	0.61	$Cu^{+0.2}I^{-0.2}$	0.79
$In^{+0.7}As^{-0.7}$	0.42	$Ag^{+0.2}I^{-0.2}$	0.81
$In^{0}Sb^{0}$	0.24		
$(In^{-1.4}Bi^{+1.4}$	-0.11 metal)		

III VI (λ_0 III VI $= 0.25$)	
☐ $Al_2^{+1.5}S_3^{-1}$	λ III VI $= 0.50$
☐ $Al_2^{+0.3}Se_3^{-0.2}$	0.31
☐ $Al_2^{-1}Te_3^{+0.7}$	0
☐ $Ga_2^{+1.4}S_3^{-0.9}$	0.49
☐ $Ga_2^{+0.4}Se_3^{-0.3}$	0.36
☐ $Ga_2^{-0.5}Te_3^{+0.4}$	0.12
☐ $In_2^{+1.3}S_3^{-0.9}$	0.47
☐ $In_2^{+0.6}Se_3^{-0.4}$	0.40
☐ $In_2^{-0.1}Te_3^{+0.1}$	0.14

with experimental results, which we shall consider in the following sections, leads us to think that the absolute error involved is perhaps less than 0.05. However, the second decimal place is only an indicative value. The most ionic compounds are LiF and NaF ($0.93 \simeq 0.9$), and the most covalent AlSb ($0.01 \simeq 0$), Mg_2Sn ($-0.02 \simeq 0$) and Mg_3Sb_2 ($-0.03 \simeq 0$). The effective charge q is given to only one significant figure but it is easy to obtain a more precise value by using the equation $q = c(\lambda - \lambda_0)$ or the semi-empirical formula involving Z and r. The values found for InSb, ZnS and NaCl agree with those which we indicated as probable in Section 2.5 and the signs of the values found for AlSb and GaSb are in agreement with the remarks made in Section 3.4.

TABLE 7.3

($c = 4$ for the anion)

III V ($\lambda_0 = 0.25$)		II V (λ_0 II V $= 0$)	
$Tl^{-0.1}Sb^{+0.1}$ $\lambda = 0.21$		□ $Mg_3^{+1.2}P_2^{-1.8}$ λ II V $= 0.61$	
$Tl^{-1.3}Bi^{+1.3}$ -0.08 metal		□ $Mg_3^{+0.6}As_2^{-0.9}$ 0.29	
		□ $Mg_3^{-0.1}Sb_2^{+0.1}$ -0.03 metal	
I VII ($\lambda_0 = 0.75$)		□ $Mg_3^{-1.2}Bi_2^{+1.8}$ -0.61 metal	
$Cs^{+0.5}Cl^{-0.5}$ $\lambda = 0.88$		□ $Zn_3^{+1.1}P_2^{-1.7}$ 0.55	
$Cs^{+0.4}Br^{-0.4}$ 0.85		□ $Zn_3^{+0.5}As_2^{-0.8}$ 0.27	
$Cs^{+0.3}I^{-0.3}$ 0.83		□ $Zn_3^0Sb_2^0$ 0	
		□ $Zn_3^{-1}Bi_2^{+1.5}$ -0.51 metal	
II IV ($\lambda_0 = 0$)		□ $Cd_3^{+1}P_2^{-1.6}$ 0.52	
$Mg_2^{+1.2}Si^{-2.5}$ $\lambda = 0.63$		□ $Cd_3^{+0.6}As_2^{-0.9}$ 0.32	
$Mg_2^{+0.6}Ge^{-1.2}$ 0.30		□ $Cd_3^{+0.2}Sb_2^{-0.3}$ 0.12	
$Mg_2^0Sn^{+0.1}$ -0.02		□ $Cd_3^{-0.5}Bi_2^{+0.8}$ -0.27 metal	
$Mg_2^{-1.1}Pb^{+2.3}$ -0.57 metal			

TABLE 7.4

($c = 3$)

Di-electronic: IV VI ($\lambda_0 = 0.33$)

$Ge^{+1.1}S^{-1.1}$ $\lambda = 0.70$	$Sn^{+1}S^{-1}$ $\lambda = 0.67$
$Ge^{+0.6}Se^{-0.6}$ 0.54	$Sn^{+0.7}Se^{-0.7}$ 0.56

Mono-electronic:

II$_A$ VI and IV VI ($\lambda_0 = 0.33$)		I$_A$ VII and I VII ($\lambda_0 = 0.67$)	
$Mg^{+1.5}O^{-1.5}$ $\lambda = 0.82$		$Li^{+0.8}F^{-0.8}$ $\lambda = 0.93$	
$Mg^{+1.2}S^{-1.2}$ 0.73		$Li^{+0.6}Cl^{-0.6}$ 0.88	
$Mg^{+0.6}Se^{-0.6}$ 0.52		$Li^{+0.3}Br^{-0.3}$ 0.76	
$Ca^{+1.5}O^{-1.5}$ 0.80		$Li^{-0.1}I^{+0.1}$ 0.64	
$Ca^{+1.3}S^{-1.3}$ 0.78		$Na^{+0.8}F^{-0.8}$ 0.93	
$Ca^{+0.9}Se^{-0.9}$ 0.64		$Na^{+0.7}Cl^{-0.7}$ 0.90	
$Ca^{+0.5}Te^{-0.5}$ 0.50		$Na^{+0.5}Br^{-0.5}$ 0.83	
$Sr^{+1.2}O^{-1.2}$ 0.73		$Na^{+0.3}I^{-0.3}$ 0.76	
$Sr^{+1.2}S^{-1.2}$ 0.72		$K^{+0.7}F^{-0.7}$ 0.92	
$Sr^{+0.8}Se^{-0.8}$ 0.60		$K^{+0.7}Cl^{-0.7}$ 0.91	
$Ba^{+0.9}O^{-0.9}$ 0.64		$K^{+0.6}Br^{-0.6}$ 0.86	
$Ba^{+1}S^{-1}$ 0.66		$K^{+0.4}I^{-0.4}$ 0.81	
$Ba^{+0.7}Se^{-0.7}$ 0.57		$Rb^{+0.6}F^{-0.6}$ 0.87	
$Ba^{+0.5}Te^{-0.5}$ 0.49		$Rb^{+0.6}Cl^{-0.6}$ 0.87	
$Ge^{-0.5}Te^{+0.5}$ 0.15		$Rb^{+0.5}Br^{-0.5}$ 0.83	
$Sn^{-0.3}Te^{+0.3}$ 0.24		$Rb^{+0.4}I^{-0.4}$ 0.79	
$Pb^{+0.6}S^{-0.6}$ 0.55		$Cs^{+0.5}F^{-0.5}$ 0.82	
$Pb^{+0.4}Se^{-0.4}$ 0.46		$Ag^{+0.5}F^{-0.5}$ 0.84	
$Pb^{+0.2}Te^{-0.2}$ 0.39		$Ag^{+0.5}Cl^{-0.5}$ 0.85	
		$Ag^{+0.4}Br^{-0.4}$ 0.80	

In each series the light elements have formulae $M^{+|q|}X^{-|q|}$ which express a qualitative displacement of charges in conformity with an ionic distribution. As the atomic weight increases, the increase of Z always outweighs that of r in the formulae giving q, which brings about a virtual neutral formula M^0X^0, then a formula $M^{-|q|}X^{+|q|}$ of opposite polarity representing a qualitative charge displacement in conformity with a covalent distribution. This is simply the result of the mutual polarization of the electron clouds whose interpenetration results in a return toward a covalent nature. However, in the case of strong polarization of one of the atoms, one of the terms Z/r' or Z'/r becomes negligible and the other atom only enters into the formula through its radius. Increasing the atomic weight of this atom thus increases the ionicity instead of diminishing it (diminution of the polarization). Polarization of the anion occurs more frequently because of its greater dimensions (on average $1/r \simeq 3/r'$). Thus BN, 0·54; AlN, 0·77; GaSb, 0·13 and InSb, 0·24; CuI, 0·79 and AgI, 0·81; SnTe, 0·24 and PbTe, 0·39; LiI, 0·64 and NaI, 0·76 etc. . . . However, the anion sometimes has some effect: BaO, 0·64 and BaS, 0·66; AgF, 0·84 and AgCl, 0·85.

Because of our basic hypothesis the probability λ is necessarily a positive number lying between 0 and 1. A negative value would correspond to a transfer of sedentary electrons from X toward M which is incompatible with original hypotheses. It is particularly noteworthy that the negative values of λ correspond, without any exceptions, to metallic compounds. Thus we can now give the two conditions under which semiconductivity appears:

(1) Existence of a covalent bonding scheme compatible with the crystallographic structure (cf. Chapter 4).
(2) Parameter λ positive.

Compounds such as InBi or Mg_2Pb satisfy the first condition, but not the second.

In Section 4.3 we saw how we could derive ternary compounds by isoelectronic substitution from a binary compound. Tables 7.5, 7.6 and 7.7 give the average effective charges carried by the anion and the ionicities of the two bonds for three series of ternary compounds derived from the binary III–V, II–VI and IV–VI compounds respectively. The first two, with general formulae I IV VI_2 and I III VI_2, crystallize in the *E1* structure of chalcopyrite (co-ordination 4) and the latter, of general formula I V VI_2, in the *B1* rocksalt structure or the $F5_6$ structure of wolfsbergite (co-ordination 3 and resonance). The definition of mean charge on the anion presupposes that the cation distribution is ordered. All the compounds shown in these tables have not been studied and it is quite possible that some of them do not exist. The description 'metallic' is only a forecast [7.4], [7.5], [7.6], [7.7].

TABLE 7.5

Compound	q'	λ_1	λ_2
II IV P$_2$	$-1\cdot1$ to $-1\cdot4$	0·76 to 0·78	0·31 to 0·42
Cd Sn As$_2$	$-0\cdot6$	0·66	0·15
Zn Sn As$_2$	$-0\cdot6$	0·64	0·15
Cd Pb As$_2$	$-0\cdot5$	0·66	0·08
Zn Pb As$_2$	$-0\cdot5$	0·64	0·08
Cd Ge As$_2$	$-0\cdot4$	0·66	0·04
Zn Ge As$_2$	$-0\cdot4$	0·64	0·04
Cd Si As$_2$	$-0\cdot2$	0·66	$-0\cdot09$
Zn Si As$_2$	$-0\cdot2$	0·64	$-0\cdot09$
II IV Sb$_2$		∼0·53	<0 metallic

TABLE 7.6

Compound	q'	λ_1	λ_2
I III S$_2$	$-0\cdot8$ to $-1\cdot0$	0·88 to 0·90	0·51 to 0·63
I Tl Se$_2$	$-0\cdot6$	0·85	0·43
I In Se$_2$	$-0\cdot5$	0·85	0·40
I Ga Se$_2$	$-0\cdot4$	0·85	0·36
I Al Se$_2$	$-0\cdot3$	0·85	0·32
Ag Tl Te$_2$	$-0\cdot4$	0·81	0·39
Cu Tl Te$_2$	$-0\cdot3$	0·77	0·39
Ag In Te$_2$	$-0\cdot1$	0·81	0·22
Cu In Te$_2$	0	0·77	0·22
Ag Ga Te$_2$	0·2	0·81	0·11
Cu Ga Te$_2$	0·2	0·77	0·11
Ag Al Te$_2$	0·4	0·81	0
Cu Al Te$_2$	0·5	0·77	0

7.3 Chemical Interpretation of the Energy Gap

In Section 6.4 some empirical relations between various chemical parameters and the energy gap were given. Here we are going to try to give a coherent chemical interpretation for this energy [7.8]. Returning first to the ideas of Zhuze and Manca, we shall base our arguments upon the heat of formation from the elements, then for compounds we shall use the parameter λ defined above.

TABLE 7.7

Compound	q'	λ_1	λ_2
I V S_2	-0.9 to -1.4	0.84 to 0.87	0.25 to 0.51
I Sb Se_2	-0.7	0.80	0.23
I As Se_2	-0.7	0.80	0.23
I Bi Se_2	-0.5	0.80	0.10
I P Se_2	-0.4	0.80	0.11
Ag Sb Te_2	-0.2	0.75	0.01
Cu Sb Te_2	-0.1	0.69	0.01
Ag As Te_2	0	0.75	-0.05
Cu As Te_2	0	0.69	-0.05
Ag Bi Te_2	0	0.75	-0.07
Cu Bi Te_2	0.1	0.69	-0.07
I P Te_2		0.69 to 0.75	<0 metallic

Let us begin by considering the case of those elements whose crystals are made up with purely covalent bonds. The sum of the energies $e_1, e_2, \ldots e_o$ necessary for the successive excitation of the c bonding electrons of an atom out of the orbitals corresponds to the standard heat of formation Q of the crystal from its atoms, divided by Avogadro's number G. It is readily seen that the first energy e_1, the only one in which we are interested, will be smaller than the average energy Q/Gc. If we plot E_G as a function of Q/Gc (Fig. 7.2), the existence of an equation of the following form is clearly shown:

$$e = (Q/Gc - 0.63) \text{ eV}.$$

However, e only represents a fraction of the energy gap, which would appear to be given by the relationship

$$E_G = \eta(Q/Gc - 0.63) \text{ eV}.$$

The appearance of η, the number of valence electrons possessed by the element, undoubtedly indicates a mutual interaction of the electrons in this level which increases the energy required for the liberation of one of them. We used the values of the bond energies $2Q/c$ for the two atoms appearing in Table 6.6 in order to calculate Q/Gc and the values of E_G at room temperature were taken from Table 6.1 or from HANNAY [6]. The energy gaps given for phosphorus and arsenic were measured on thin layers and are very uncertain.

Let us consider the case of simple binary compounds crystallizing in the blende structure, the only ones for which E_G is known with some precision.

In Fig. 7.3, E_G is plotted on a semi-logarithmic scale as a function of the crystalline ionicity λ. The points representing compounds of the same series such as AlN, AlP, AlAs and AlSb define straight lines which allow us to extrapolate values of E_G for $\lambda = 0$ or $\lambda = 1$. For $\lambda = 0$, we have ideal crystals where the atoms have four electrons such as Al⁻, Zn²⁻, etc. .... and form purely covalent bonds with the highly polarizable

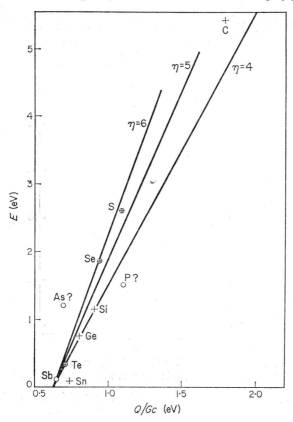

FIG. 7.2. Energy gaps for the elemental semiconductors
(following SUCHET [7.8])

heavy metalloids. Their energy gaps appear to be arranged in more or less opposite order to that of the number of electrons, $Z = 14$ (Si, Al⁻), 32 (Ge, Ga⁻, Zn²⁻), 50 (Sn, In⁻, Cd²⁻). For $\lambda = 1$ we have ideal crystals where the light ions with perfect electron octets form purely ionic bonds. The corresponding energy gaps seem to be slightly greater than 5 eV.

Thus for these compounds we can distinguish two contributions to the energy gap E_G: a covalent contribution E_1, characteristic of the metallic atom M, and, for the compounds considered, a virtually constant ionic contribution E_2, characteristic of a small and strongly electropositive atom such as a light halogen X. Thus it is tempting to apply the relationships found above in terms of η and Q/Gc to an array of M⁻ or M²⁻ atoms (4 electrons) in order to calculate the first contribution, and to an array of X⁻ atoms (8 electrons) in order to calculate the second contribution. We must take into account in each case the additional energy introduced by the electron affinity of the neutral atom for the supplementary electron or electrons [7.9]. Unfortunately, we do not have at our disposal any

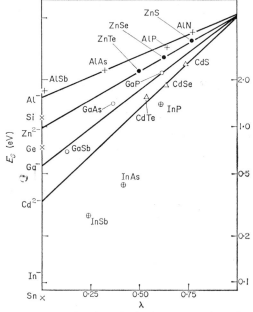

FIG. 7.3. Energy gaps for the principal compound semiconductors crystallizing in the blende structure (after SUCHET [7.8])

indications as to what might be the standard heat of formation for metallic atoms linked by tetrahedral covalent bonds. The most that we can suggest is that it will be of the same order as that of the corresponding element in the fourth column of the classification, so that the weak affinity of these metals would not make E_1 much different from the corresponding values of E_G for Si, Ge and Sn. This has been well verified. For the second term, one finds from the standard heats of formation of the F_2, Cl_2 and Br_2 molecules:

$$1\cdot31 + 3\cdot63 \simeq 4\cdot9 \text{ eV (F}^-)$$
$$1\cdot26 + 3\cdot78 \simeq 5\cdot0 \text{ eV (Cl}^-)$$
$$1\cdot04 + 3\cdot54 \simeq 4\cdot6 \text{ eV (Br}^-)$$

The order of magnitude of 5 eV agrees well with that indicated in Fig. 7.3.

If one supposes, as is suggested by this figure, that the experimental points relative to compounds of the same metal are reasonably well arranged on straight lines, one is led to the following relations:

$$\log E_G - \log E_1 = \lambda(\log E_2 - \log E_1)$$

whence:
$$E_G = E_1^{1-\lambda} E_2^\lambda$$

One notes that $1 - \lambda$ and λ are simply the respective probabilities p_i for the electron distributions responsible for the E_i contributions, and that their sum is necessarily unity, hence:

$$E_G = \Pi E_i^{p_i}$$

7.4 The Propagation of Electrons and Phonons

In Section 2.3, and later in Section 6.1, we saw that the propagation of electrons in a semiconducting crystal having a specified concentration of carriers of one type depended on the **mobility** of these carriers. That is to say, it depends on a property characteristic of the crystal, and as such, related to the type of chemical bonds which are present. In Section 6.1 we mentioned a **polar scattering** mechanism which arose from the charges carried by the atoms of the lattice. If the influence of this scattering upon the mobility is important, the considerations set out in the first two sections of this chapter show that μ must be a maximum for $\lambda = \lambda_0$, that is to say $q = (q/c) = 0$, in each series of compounds. Figures 7.4, 7.5, 7.6 and 7.7 display the logarithmic variation of the electron mobility as a function of λ for the III V, II VI, I VII and IV VI compounds. We have separated those series whose parameters c and λ_0 do not have the same value, so as to show the occurrence of a maximum more clearly [7.10], [7.11]. Most of the values of mobility are taken from Table 6.1 or from BUBE [7]. Those for SnS [7.12], SnTe [7.13] and GeTe [7.14] are taken from the literature. In each figure we see that to the right of the point $\lambda = \lambda_0$, the metallic atom has a positive charge and the mobility decreases rapidly as this charge increases. To the left of this point, the metallic atom has a negative charge and once more the mobility decreases. Thus these figures corroborate the concepts set out above.

In Section 6.1 we also mentioned non-polar scattering caused by the thermal vibrations of the atoms. The amplitude of these vibrations (which is inseparable from the idea of temperature) varies from atom to atom in a periodic manner, and suggests the idea of a wave propagated through the crystal. The name **phonons** is used to denote these waves. Amongst the possible types of vibration we may distinguish those having large energies and propagating at small velocities (so-called optical modes) and vibrations of small energy propagating with high velocities (so-called acoustic modes). Experimentally, the former manifest themselves by infra-red absorption effects. For every direction in the crystal, a velocity corresponding to the propagation of one longitudinal and two transverse waves for the acoustic modes can be determined, and an average velocity of propagation (the velocity of sound or the shear-wave velocity) obtained. The existence of acoustic phonons is demonstrated most clearly by the energy transport for which they are responsible (thermal conductivity). These phonons are responsible principally for the non-polar scattering of electrons; hence the term **acoustic scattering** is often given to this phenomenon.

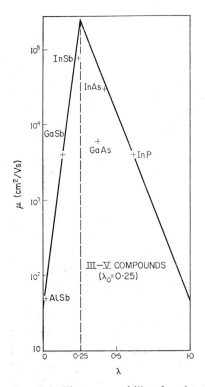

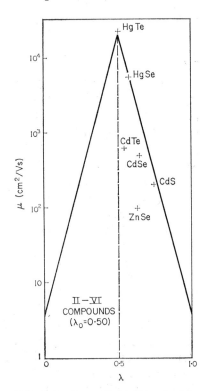

FIG. 7.4. Electron mobility for the III V compounds (following SUCHET *et al.* [7.11])

FIG. 7.5. Electron mobility for the II VI compounds (following SUCHET *et al.* [7.11])

Let us concentrate our attention on those simple binary compounds whose atoms carry an effective charge of exactly zero. We may deduce their mobility from the maximum of each curve, that is to say a value slightly greater than that of InSb for III V compounds, the value corresponding to HgTe for the II VI compounds and a value extrapolated from the mobilities of the potassium and silver halides for the I VII compounds. These three points are plotted in Fig. 7.8 and indicate a rapid decrease of mobility as the ionicity of the compounds increases. Since the effect of polar scattering has now been eliminated, this decrease is characteristic of the acoustic scattering and we shall call the mobility obtained from this figure the **acoustic mobility.** It varies as:

$$\mu_{acoust.} = \alpha \, \exp \, (-\beta\lambda)$$

where $\alpha \simeq 3\cdot 10^6$ and $\beta = 9\cdot 6$. In the atoms of the IV VI compounds, the presence of a pair of s electrons taking no part in bonds may explain the

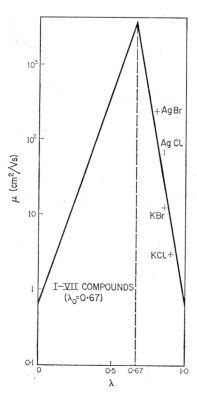

FIG. 7.6. Electron mobility for the I VII compounds (following SUCHET *et al.* [7.11])

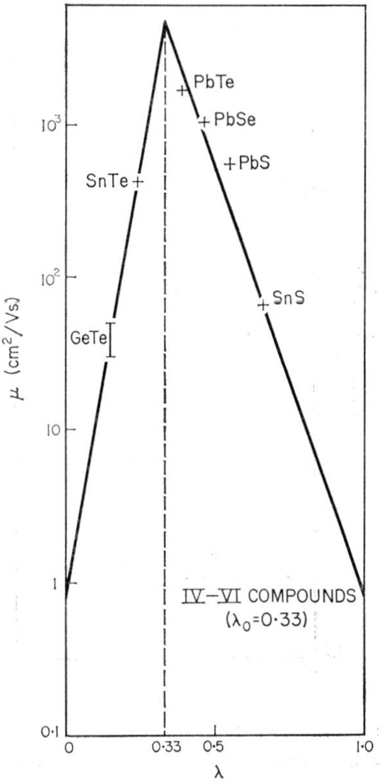

FIG. 7.7. Electron mobility for the IV VI compounds (following SUCHET [7.10])

displacement of their representative point. For Ge and Si the mobilities are limited by some other mechanism, probably optical phonons, whose importance in this role is difficult to explain on the basis of the approximate crystallo-chemical model alone (cf. Appendix).

We shall now account for the mobility variations shown in Figs. 7.4 to 7.7 by superimposing the effects of the two scattering mechanisms considered above. Assigning in each figure the maximum value of acoustic mobility plotted in Fig. 7.8, we shall define a **polar mobility** such that for each compound:*

$$\log \mu = \log \mu_{\text{acoust.}} - \log \mu_{\text{polar}}$$

It is clear that the second term, which is determined only by the polar scattering, is not a function of the polarity q/c since the various straight lines do not have the same slope. It is a function of the quotient of this quantity with the maximum possible polarity, that is to say, the relative

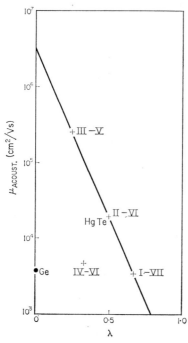

FIG. 7.8. Acoustic mobility in binary compounds (following SUCHET *et al.* [7.11])

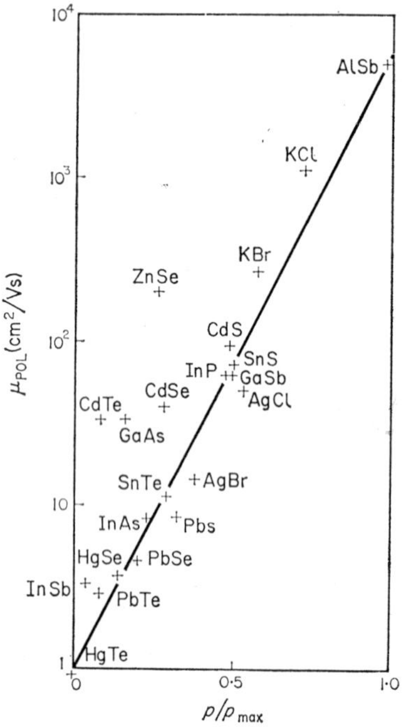

FIG. 7.9. Polar mobility in the binary compounds (following SUCHET *et al.* [7.11])

polarity $(q/c)(q/c)_{\text{max.}}$ or, in other words, the relative effective charge $q/q_{\text{max.}}$. In Section 7.1 we saw that the effective charge q carried by an atom lies between the limits $+n$ and $-m$, whence:

$$q/q_{\text{max.}} = q/n \qquad \text{if } q > 0$$
$$q/q_{\text{max.}} = -q/m \quad \text{if } q < 0$$

* More exactly, if one considers the additivity of the two terms $(1/\mu_1 + 1/\mu_2)$, one obtains:

$$\log \mu = \log \mu_1 - \log (1 + \mu_1/\mu_2)$$

Figure 7.9 shows the exponential relationship obtained

$$\mu_{pol.} = \exp \gamma(q/q_{max.})$$

where γ is of the order of 8·7. In this way, by combining the relationships found for $\mu_{acoust.}$ and $\mu_{pol.}$ one obtains:

$$\mu = \alpha \exp [-\beta\lambda_0 - \gamma(q/q_{max.})]$$

or $\qquad \mu \simeq 3.10^6/\exp 9(\lambda_0 + q/q_{max.}) \text{ cm}^2/\text{Vs}.$

Returning to the propagation of phonons: if this depends on the ionicity, we must retrieve an analogous correlation with the thermal conductivity k. However, the latter is a complex physical property and is influenced by many factors. In the following discussion we shall suppose that the lattice contribution to k dominates the conductivity, leaving aside any contribution due to the electrons. From the outset we eliminate the influence of the atomic mass of the constituent atoms by considering the product kA, where A is the average atomic weight, i.e. the atomic thermal conductivity at ambient temperatures. The semi-logarithmic graph in Fig. 7.10 shows the distribution of these points and indicates a very approximate relationship of the form:

$$kA \simeq \alpha \exp (-\beta\lambda)$$

resembling that found for $\mu_{acoust.}$, but with $\beta = 4·7$. The values of k are taken from Table 6.1, with the exception of the values for Ge, Si, CdTe, HgSe, HgTe [7.15], Bi_3Sb [7.16] and for GeTe [7.14]. It appears that the electronic structure has some influence, one of the lines being delineated by C, Ge, InSb, CdTe (shared pairs only) and the other by Bi_3Sb (solid solution Bi–Sb), GeTe and PbTe (s unshared pair). However, the alkali halides are displaced away from the former line.

Let us now consider a ternary compound $M'M''X_2$ obtained from the MX binary compound by isoelectronic substitution for the M cation. Thus we replace the M–X bond by two bonds M'–X and M''–X whose ionicities are respectively greater and less than that of M–X. Experiments show that the order of magnitude of k is always much smaller than for the corresponding binary compound. Since the thermal conductivity seems to be limited by the ionicity λ, we have considered attributing this diminution to the increase of ionicity as one passes from M–X to M'–X. In Fig. 7.11, only the highest ionicity has been taken into consideration and we can see that the shift of the representative point confirms the experimental law suggested and the value for the coefficient β given above, when we pass from InAs to $CdSnAs_2$, from CdTe to $AgInTe_2$, from PbSe to $AgSbSe_2$ and from PbTe to $AgSbTe_2$.

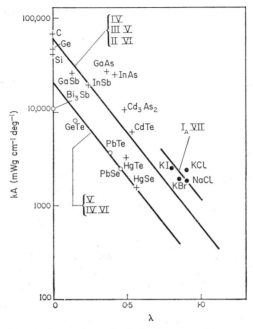

FIG. 7.10. Atomic thermal conductivity for some binary compounds
(following SUCHET *et al.* [7.11])

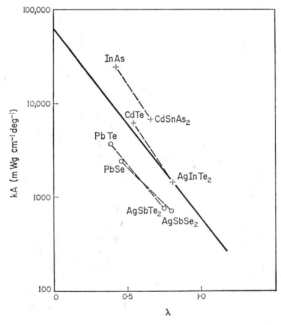

FIG. 7.11. Atomic thermal conductivity of some ternary compounds
(following SUCHET *et al.* [7.11])

7.5 Application to the Search for New Materials

The search for new semiconducting materials lies essentially within the province of the chemist, but because he is faced with a multiplicity of possible compounds he needs to be guided by certain general principles. This is the *raison d'être* for the crystallochemical model set out in this chapter. We are going to show how it can be used, for example, in the search for magneto-electric and thermo-electric ternary materials [7.11].

Magneto-electric effects arise from the action of a magnetic field upon currents flowing perpendicularly to this field. The application of a perpendicular field to the plate shown in Fig. 7.12, results in an increase in the resistance met by the current flowing along it (magneto-resistance effect), and the appearance of a potential difference between the faces A and B

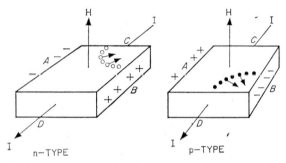

Fig. 7.12. Magneto-electric effects in a semiconductor plate

(Hall effect). The utilization of these effects in various electronic devices (gauss meters, gyrators) is conditioned by the existence of materials with high electron mobilities such as InSb or InAs [7.17].

We saw in the preceding section that a high mobility is achieved when the polar scattering is zero or negligible (effective charges virtually zero) and when acoustic scattering is weak (small atomic ionicity). If, for example, we examine the three series of ternary compounds discussed in Section 7.2, Tables 7.5, 7.6 and 7.7 show us that an effective average charge of zero on the anion can only exist for the antimonides and tellurides. However, the first are excluded because of their probable metallic nature (λ found negative for the IV–Sb bond). Furthermore, small effective charges, of the order of 0·5, occur in the arsenides and selenides. As far as acoustic scattering is concerned, we see immediately that the arsenides, deriving from the III V compound ($\lambda_0 = 0.25$), will be much more suitable than the selenides and tellurides, deriving from the IV VI compounds ($\lambda_0 = 0.33$) or II VI compounds ($\lambda_0 = 0.50$). Examination of the curves given in Section 7.4 shows that one gains a factor of ten in the acoustic mobility by adopting $\lambda_0 = 0.25$ instead of 0·33 or 0·50 whilst one only loses a factor of two in the polar mobility by accepting an effective charge of 0·5, that is to say a polarity of the order of 0·1 to 0·15. Thus we would undertake the synthesis of the arsenides II IV As$_2$ where II = Cd or Zn and IV = Sn, Pb or Ge. In fact a mobility of 12,000 cm^2/Vs at ambient temperature has been found for CdSnAs$_2$ [7.18].

The thermo-electric effects arise from the effect of a temperature gradient on the concentration of charge carriers. Suppose that the latter may be regarded as a perfect gas enclosed within a cylinder at temperature T. If one of the ends of this cylinder is heated to a temperature $T + dT$ and the other cooled to $T - dT$ the gas occupying the heated end will expand and that in the cooled end contract, so that the number of electrons N or of holes P leaving any region will be much smaller at the high temperature end (Fig. 7.13).

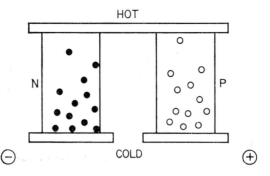

FIG. 7.13. Thermo-electric effects in two semiconductor cylinders

This results in the appearance of a potential difference between the two ends of a semiconductor subjected to a temperature gradient (Seebeck effect). At a junction between semiconductors of opposite conductivity type the passage of a current may liberate or absorb heat (Peltier effect).

The utilization of these effects in various devices (thermopiles, electronic refrigerators) is conditioned by the existence of materials having large values of the ratio μ/k of mobility to thermal conductivity, such as Bi$_2$Te$_3$ [7.19].

We saw in the preceding section that it was possible to obtain very low atomic thermal conductivity kA by taking ternary compounds M'M''X$_2$ where the M'–X bond had a high ionicity. Tables 7.5 to 7.7 show that this condition is realized in compounds derived from the II VI and IV VI compounds where the ionicities λ_1 lie between 0·69 to 0·90. On the other hand the polar mobility can only be annulled for the tellurides, thus our choice is immediately limited. With the I III Te$_2$ compounds, we have a relatively high thermal conductivity (upper line in Fig. 7.10) and, with the I V Te$_2$

compounds, we can count on a very small k (lower line in the same figure): we would prepare by preference $AgSbTe_2$ to avoid the compounds of arsenic and bismuth which are probably metallic. In fact, the compound $AgSbTe_2$ has been proposed as a thermo-element [7.20], [7.21], and is at the present time the best of the known materials for temperatures between ambient and 500°C.

Chapter 8

MAGNETIC INTERACTIONS

8.1 The Role of Magnetic Criterion

WE must consider in more detail the transition element compounds treated in Section 4.5. Figure 1.1 shows that the energy of the $3d$ level is intermediate between those of the $4s$ levels and $4p$ levels, with consequently a very large number of possible electron exchanges and hybrid bonding orbitals: d-s, d-p and d-s-p. To clarify this complicated situation, it is essential to use to its fullest extent the information provided by the study of the magnetic properties of these compounds.

For compounds with unpaired electrons we can distinguish two regions on either side of a transition temperature: the **coupling region** at low temperatures where there are ferromagnetic or antiferromagnetic interactions between the spins of these electrons, and the **paramagnetic region** at high temperature where these interactions are destroyed by thermal agitation. The transition point (the Curie or Néel point) is often referred to as the coupling temperature T_c, and we shall use this name. The temperature variation of the molar magnetic susceptibility (the product of the susceptibility and the sum of the atomic weights of the different atoms including

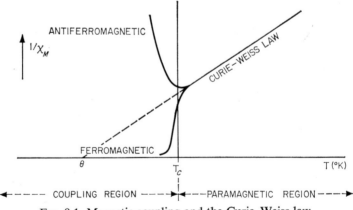

FIG. 8.1. Magnetic coupling and the Curie–Weiss law
(following SUCHET [8.2])

134

one magnetic atom) readily allows one to recognize these regions (Fig. 8.1). In the paramagnetic region, the molar susceptibility satisfies a simple law, the so-called **Curie–Weiss law.**

$$\chi_M = C/(T - \theta)$$

and the parameter θ may be determined by plotting $1/\chi_M$ against T.

The Langevin theory of paramagnetism, together with the Weiss theory, gives the following expression for the susceptibility in the general weak field case:

$$\chi_M = G\mathcal{M}^2/3k(T - \theta)$$

where G is Avogadro's number, $\mathcal{M}$ the magnetic moment averaged per magnetic atom, and k Boltzmann's constant. We can rearrange this expression, introducing the Bohr magneton, β_m:

$$\mathcal{M}/\beta_m = (1/\beta_m)\sqrt{3k\chi_M(T - \theta)/G}$$

$$\mathcal{M} \simeq 2{\cdot}83\sqrt{\chi_M(T - \theta)} \text{ magnetons}$$

This moment depends upon the magnetic state of the atoms, that is to say the manner in which the orbital moments (due to the orbiting of the electrons around the nucleus) and the spin moments (due to the intrinsic moment of the electrons themselves) of several electrons are coupled to one another to form the resultant moment of the atom. For weak magnetic fields, which do not disturb this coupling, it can be described in terms of a simplified vectorial model in which each electron has angular momentum vectors of $(h/2\pi)\sqrt{l(l + 1)}$ and $(h/2\pi)\sqrt{s(s + 1)}$ corresponding with orbital and spin motion respectively. l is here the second (azimuthal) quantum number, which can take integral values from zero up to one less than the principal quantum number, and s is the electron spin quantum number, equal to $\frac{1}{2}$. The most important mode of coupling is known as Russell-Saunders, and in it the l and s vectors are coupled strongly in separate respective groups to give vectorial resultants denoted by L and S (equal to $(h/2\pi)\sqrt{L(L + 1)}$ and $(h/2\pi)\sqrt{S(S + 1)}$ respectively), where L is a positive integer (or zero) and S is a positive half integer (or zero); these are then weakly coupled to give a resultant J (angular momentum $(h/2\pi)\sqrt{J(J + 1)}$), which takes one of the values

$$L + S, L + S - 1, \ldots, |L - S|$$

A particular atomic state is associated with given L, S, J (not necessarily uniquely). Both spin and orbital motion are associated with magnetic moments, and the quantum theory of magnetism leads to an expression for the resultant magnetic moment, or the number of magnetons:

$$\mathcal{M} = g\sqrt{J(J + 1)}$$

with $g = 1 + [J(J + 1) + S(S + 1) - L(L + 1)]/2J(J + 1)$. These expressions are greatly simplified when the orbital motions are quenched and

$L = 0$, which is approximately the case in the transition element compounds (cf. [8.1]). Then, g is equal to 2 and $J = S$:

$$\mathscr{M} \simeq 2\sqrt{S(S + 1)}$$

Note that, *if all s vectors are parallel, S/s represents the number of unpaired* electrons with uncompensated spin. Since $s = \frac{1}{2}$, this number is simply $2S$. By equating the two expressions found for the molecular moment one easily obtains:

$$\mathscr{M} \simeq 2\cdot 83\sqrt{\chi_M(T - \theta)} \simeq \sqrt{2S(2S + 2)}$$

whence the expression given by SUCHET [8.2]:

$$\boxed{2S \simeq \sqrt{1 + 8\chi_M(T - \theta)} - 1}$$

A knowledge of the number of unpaired electrons is information of the greatest interest with respect to the way in which an atom is bound to its neighbours. It is this that we call the **magnetic criterion.** Let us consider, for example, the cobalt atom. Table 1.1 shows us that its electronic formula is $3d^7 4s^2$. Let us enquire what will be the electronic formula for the isolated Co^{4+} ion, i.e. in a vacuum or in a dilute solution. Once the s and two of the d electrons are removed, there remain 5 electrons in d levels. Hund's rules, which may be applied to ions as well as to atoms so long as they are isolated, tell us that these 5 electrons will occupy the greatest number of possible states, so that each of them will occupy one of the 5 states of the d level, Fig. 8.2. Now let us enquire what is the electronic formula of the cobalt atom in a crystal of the compound $CoAs_2$. This compound, as we shall see in the following section, crystallizes in the $C2$ pyrite structure and the covalent nature of the interatomic bonds brings into play $d^2 sp^3$ orbital hybrids for the cobalt atom and sp^3 for the arsenic atom, with an As–As bond. If for the moment we picture the ionic character of these same bonds we are led to speak of a Co^{4+} ion, but it is quite evident that this simply refers to a hypothetical electron distribution, i.e. to an over-simplified point of view. Hund's rules cannot be used to find the electronic formula for a partially ionic scheme, since they are only concerned with isolated ions or atoms. The electronic occupation of the three d states which do not participate in the bonds is thus the same as in the covalent arrangement.

Thus we see that *there can be no question of using the magnetic criterion to say whether a crystal has a more covalent or more ionic character.* This error, which appeared in the first edition of PAULING's book [8.3], has since been corrected both there and elsewhere. On the other hand, this criterion allows us to differentiate between an isolated ion and an ion forming iono-covalent bonds since the measurement of the susceptibility as a function of temperature in the first case gives $2S = 5$ and in the second

$2S = 1$. Such a criterion is evidently of interest for the study of complex ions in solution. Moreover, supposing that we are hesitating over the choice of a covalent scheme to attribute to a crystal, the criterion will help us if the number of unpaired electrons differs among the possible schemes. We shall often have occasion to use the criterion in this way in the following sections.

Having made these preliminary remarks, it is always possible to apply

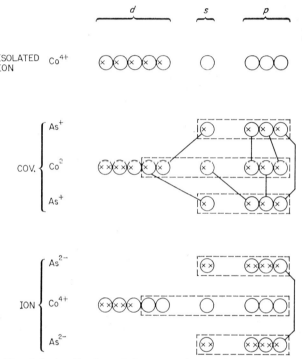

FIG. 8.2. Application of the magnetic criterion to Co^{4+}
(following SUCHET [8.2])

the crystallochemical model described in the preceding chapter to a compound in which one knows with certainty the covalent bond scheme. Table 8.1 gives the values of Z and of $1/r$ for the compounds of the transition elements serving as a basis for the calculation of the effective charges. The values of c and λ_0 are deduced from the crystallographic structure and we shall return to the structures considered in Section 4.5 to indicate their values as well as those for various other known compounds.

8.2 Principal Transition Element Compounds

The structures of the transition element chalcogenides have been studied by HARALDSEN (amongst others) [8.4]; they are always hexa-co-ordinated

Table 8.1

Z	$1/r$			$1/r'$				Z'
18	Ca²⁺ 1·01	Sc³⁺ 1·23	Ti⁴⁺ 1·47	C⁴⁻ 0·385	N³⁻ 0·585	O²⁻ 0·715	F⁻ 0·736	10
19	Sc²⁺ 1·05	Ti³⁺ 1·32	V⁴⁺ 1·67					
20	Ti²⁺ 1·11	V³⁺ 1·35	Cr⁴⁺ 1·79	Si⁴⁻ 0·369	P³⁻ 0·472	S²⁻ 0·543	Cl⁻ 0·553	18
21	V²⁺ 1·14	Cr³⁺ 1·45	Mn⁴⁺ 1·85					
22	Cr²⁺ 1·19	Mn³⁺ 1·52	Fe⁴⁺ 1·89					
23	Mn²⁺ 1·25	Fe³⁺ 1·56	Co⁴⁺ 1·92	Ge⁴⁻ 0·368	As³⁻ 0·451	Se²⁻ 0·505	Br⁻ 0·513	36
24	Fe²⁺ 1·32	Co³⁺ 1·59	Ni⁴⁺ 1·92					
25	Co²⁺ 1·35	Ni³⁺ 1·61	Cu⁴⁺ 1·96					
26	Ni²⁺ 1·39	Cu³⁺ (1·64)	Zn⁴⁺ 1·96	Sn⁴⁻ 0·340	Sb³⁻ 0·408	Te²⁻ 0·453	I⁻ 0·463	54
27	Cu²⁺ (1·39)	Zn³⁺ (1·64)	Ga⁴⁺ 1·92					
28	Zn²⁺ 1·35	Ga³⁺ 1·61	Ge⁴⁺ 1·89					

It is assumed that S⁻ ∼ Cl⁻, Se⁻ ∼ Br⁻, Te⁻ ∼ I⁻, Pb²⁻ ∼ S²⁻, etc. . . .

($c = 3$, with resonance) in the case of compounds with simple formulae TX, whether they have the $B1$ rocksalt structure or one of the more or less deformed structures such as $B8$ (nickel arsenide, NiAs) or $B31$ (MnP). Sometimes there is a continuous transition up to a formula TX_2 crystallizing in the $C6$ structure (CdI_2), and it is logical to consider the latter, as well as the neighbouring $C19$ structure ($CdCl_2$), as derived vacancy lattices (with metallic vacancies $\square$), in the same way as those of intermediate composition T_2X_3 (Fig. 8.3). PEARSON [8.5] arguing on the example of MnTe,

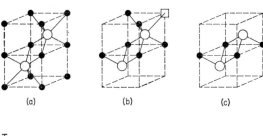

(a)   (b)   (c)

● T
○ X

FIG. 8.3. Transition between the $B8$ and $C6$ structures. Formulae TX (a), T_2X_3 (b), and TX_2 (c) (following SUCHET [8.2])

whose large thermo-electric power leaves no doubt as to its semiconducting nature, proposed for all these compounds a covalent character analogous to that of the known MX compounds crystallizing in the rocksalt structure. In Section 2.5 we introduced p^3 bonding orbitals for PbS and then supposed in Section 4.2 that for CaS and the neighbouring compounds there is an excitation of the s electrons into the p level, so as to employ again the same orbitals. In the same way we may infer from the formula of the isolated atom $3d^x s^2$ that for an atom bound in a crystal the excitation of a d electron and the s electrons into the p level leads to a distribution $3d^{x-1}p^3$. Table 8.2 gives the covalent and ionic formulae for each series of compounds on this hypothesis, as well as the electronic distribution in the d level and the number of unpaired electrons [8.2]. In this table the chemical symbols for the atoms T of the first transition series also represent the homologous elements of the other series.

We can foresee, from a calculation of the ionicity, that the T IV, FeSb, CoSb, NiSb and the TBi compounds will show metallic conductivities. The calculations indicate a semiconducting character for all the other compounds, but this is certainly not always true. Thus Pearson's hypothesis meets with some difficulty here, and its author, noting that the ratio of the axes of the unit cell of the crystal is related to the distance of the atoms T, supposed that a metallic bond would be formed between these atoms when

TABLE 8.2

Covalent formula

d level / $2S$	Ionic formula	d^0 / 0	d^1 / 1	d^2 / 2	d^3 / 3	d^4 / 4	d^5 / 5	d^6 / 4	d^7 / 3	d^8 / 2	d^9 / 1	d^{10} / 0	$s^0(p^3)/s^2(p^3)$	λ_0 τ-x
Structure:														
B8	$T^{4+}IV^{4-}$	Ti^+	V^+	Cr^+	Mn^+	Fe^+	Co^+	Ni^+	Cu^+	Zn^+	Ga^+		IV^-	-0.33
B8/B31	$T^{3+}V^{3-}$	Sc	Ti	V	Cr	Mn	Fe	Co	Ni	Cu	Zn	Ga	V	0
B1/B8	$T^{2+}VI^{2-}$	Ca^-	Sc^-	Ti^-	V^-	Cr^-	Mn^-	Fe^-	Co^-	Ni^-	Cu^-	Zn^-	VI^+	0.33
B1	T^+VII^-	K^{2-}	Ca^{2-}	Sc^{2-}	Ti^{2-}	V^{2-}	Cr^{2-}	Mn^{2-}	Fe^{2-}	Co^{2-}	Ni^{2-}	Cu^{2-}	VII^{2+}	0.67
B8/?	$\square\ T_2^{3}{}_3$	Sc_2	Ti_2	V_2	Cr_2	Mn_2	Fe_2	Co_2	Ni_2		Zn_2	Ga_2	VI_3	0
C6	$\square\ T^{4+}VI_2^{2-}{}_3$	Ti^+	V^+	Cr^+	Mn^+	Fe^+	Co^+	Ni^+		Zn^+	Ga^+	Ge^+	VI_2^+	-0.33
C6/C19	$\square\ T^{2+}VII_2^{-}{}_3$	Ca^-	Sc^-	Ti^-	V^-	Cr^-	Mn^-	Fe^-	Co^-	Ni^-	Cu^-	Zn^-	VII_2^{2+}	0.33

this ratio was smaller than the ideal value 1·63. This limiting ratio, of the order of 1·6, was also retained in spite of the exceptions arising from it by HULLIGER [8.6] who sought to extend it to the *B31* structure. A better criterion has been proposed by DUDKIN [8.7], [8.8], who considered the quantity

$$\Delta\% = 100(D - d)/d$$

where D is the shortest distance separating the two T atoms and d their diameter, and found that semiconductivity occurs for $\Delta \geqslant 14·5\%$. The weakness of such a criterion lies in knowing precisely the diameter of the T atom. The empirical values used, taken from the work on crystallo- graphy by BOKII [8.9], appear to be intermediate between PAULING'S [8.3] metallic and covalent diameters. These various criteria appear to be more uncertain than a study of the bonds and recourse to the magnetic criterion, as we shall demonstrate in the following section.

Now let us consider the compounds having formulae TX_2 and TX_3 in which the metalloid frequently has a tetrahedral environment. In the *C2* (pyrites, FeS_2 type) and *C18* (marcassite, $FeAs_2$ type) structure the T atom has a co-ordination of 6, whilst that of the X atom is only 4. Resonant bonds such as those considered by Pearson for the TX compounds, could give p^3 orbitals for the T atom and deformed sp orbitals for the X atom, but they would not account completely for the occurrence of the pure covalent X–X bond which exists in these compounds. Thus we are forced to consider di-electronic bonds and the only known orbitals comprising 6 bonding electrons are the sp^3d^2 or d^2sp^3 orbital hybrids. More precisely— for the first series of transition elements—$4sp^3d^2$ or $3d^24sp^3$. We shall designate these by α and β respectively and the corresponding iono- covalent bond schemes are represented in Fig. 8.4 for the same T atom (in CoV_2 or $MnVI_2$). We may note the condensed representation of the two schemes β, covalent and ionic, shown individually in Fig. 8.2.

The possible electronic distributions for the T atom are displayed in Table 8.3, together with the number of unpaired electrons and the ionic and covalent formulae for the various known compounds [8.2]. The chemical symbols used are those of the first transition series, but may equally well represent the elements of the other transition series. In the case of arrange- ment β, the presence in the upper d level of electrons taking no part in the bonds and not completely filling these levels results in a metallic con- ductivity (cf. Chapter 4). The magnetic criterion shows that the scheme α occurs only in the three compounds MnS_2, $MnSe_2$ and $MnTe_2$. Under these conditions the compounds $AuSb_2$, NiAsS, NiSbS and the chalco- genides of cobalt and nickel must be metallic. Calculation of the crystalline ionicity λ for the other known compounds always gives positive values, so that one does not expect any other metallic crystals. HULLIGER [8.6], and

Table 8.3

Covalent formula

Electronic formula in the α scheme

Upper level	Underlying level	2S
$(s\,d^3)$		
d^{10}	$(s\,d^3\,p^3)$	0
d^{9}	$(s\,d^3\,p^3)$	1
d^{8}	$(s\,d^3\,p^3)$	2
d^{7}	$(s\,d^3\,p^3)$	3
d^{6}	$(s\,d^3\,p^3)$	4
d^{5}	$(s\,d^3\,p^3)$	5
d^{4}	$(s^2\,d^3\,p^2)$	4
d^{3}	$(s^2\,d^3\,p^2)$	3
d^{2}	$(s^2\,d^3\,p^2)$	2
d^{1}	$(s^2\,d^3\,p^2)$	1

Electronic formula in the β scheme

Upper level	Underlying level	2S
$(s\,d^3)$		
$d^{6}(s\,d^3\,p^2)$	p^4	4
$d^{6}(s\,d^3\,p^2)$	p^3	3
$d^{6}(s\,d^3\,p^2)$	p^2	2
$d^{6}(s\,d^3\,p^2)$	p^1	1
$d^{6}(s\,d^3\,p^2)$	p^0	0
$d^{5}(s\,d^3\,p^2)$	p^0	1
$d^{4}(s\,d^3\,p^2)$	p^0	2
$d^{3}(s\,d^3\,p^2)$	p^0	3
$d^{2}(s\,d^3\,p^2)$	p^0	2
$d^{1}(s\,d^3\,p^2)$	p^0	1

Structure / Ionic formula / metallic alloys (β scheme)

Structure	Ionic formula	Metallic alloys (β scheme)	Examples	$\lambda_0\,T$–x
Unknown	$T^{6+}\ IV_2^{3-}$	IV_2	Cu^2, Zn	0
Unknown	$T^{5+}\ IV^{3-}\ V^{2-}$	$IV\ V^+$	Ni^-, Cu^-	0.17
C2/C18	$T^{4+}\ V^{2-}$	V_2^+	Cr^{2-}, Fe^{2-}, Co^{2-}, Ni^{2-}, Cu^{2-}	0.33
C2/F1	$T^{3+}\ V^{2-}\ VI^-$	$V^+\ VI^{2+}$	Fe^{3-}, Co^{3-}, Ni^{3-}	0.50
C2/C18	$T^{2+}\ VI^-$	VI_2^{2+}	Mn^{4-}, Fe^{4-}, Co^{4-}, Ni^{4-}	0.67
Unknown	$T^{+}\ VI^-\ VII$	$VI^{2+}\ VII^{3+}$	Cr^{5-}, Mn^{5-}	0.83
Unknown	$T\ VII_2$	VII_2^{3+}	V^{6-}, Cr^{6-}	1

DUDKIN and VAÏDANICH [8.10] have arrived by a similar route at the same conclusions.

The d^2sp^3-sp^3 bonds in the D2 structure (skutterudite) were examined in Section 4.5. Let us note that their ionic and covalent formulae are $Co^{3+}Sb_3^-$, $Co^{3-}Sb_3^+$, the atomic ionicity λ_0 is 0·50 for the Co–Sb bond, with a polarity $q/c = -0·07$. Thus the average polarity for Sb is $-0·03$ and from its small absolute value one can predict an appreciable mobility with respect to other compounds in the series. On the other hand the C7 structure of molybdenite MoS_2 is a layered hexagonal structure similar to the C6 structure, but its diamagnetic nature and its semiconducting

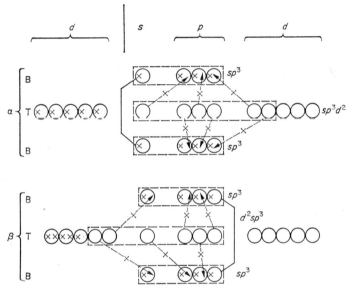

FIG. 8.4. Iono-covalent bond scheme in the C2 and C18 structures. Above: scheme α; below: scheme β (following SUCHET [8.2])

character leave no doubt about the presence of particularly unusual bonds with d^4sp orbitals for the Mo atom and p^3 orbitals for the S atom as indicated by Pauling.

To conclude let us mention the ternary compounds derived from the II VI compounds crystallizing in the chalcopyrite structure. Their formula is I T IV$_2$ where I = Cu or Ag and T is a transition element of valency 3. Here the bonds are formed with sp^3 orbitals and the d level only participates in donating an electron to the p level. The polarity, which varies slightly within a transition series, is very small for the tellurides, ranging from $-0·05$ to $+0·07$ from Ti to Ni (an electron mobility 2000 cm²/Vs has been found for $AgFeTe_2$). Other derived ternary and quarternary compounds are considered in ref. [8.2].

8.3 Polarity and Ligand Field

Let us apply the magnetic criterion to the TX compounds having rocksalt or derived structures; Table 8.4 gives a list of those compounds for which the number of uncompensated spins $2S_{exp}$ is known from the temperature variation of susceptibility or from neutron diffraction. The majority of the values are taken from the *Table of Magnetic Constants* of The International Union of Pure and Applied Chemistry [8.11], apart from those of VSe

TABLE 8.4

Structure	Compound	$2S_P$ According to the Pearson Scheme	$2S_{exp}$ From susceptibility or neutron diffraction (*)	Orbitals used
B8	CrSb	3	2·7*	p^3
B31	MnP	4	2·0	
B31	MnAs	4	3·7	p^3
B8	MnSb	4	3·53*	p^3
B31	FeP	5	2·6	
B8	CoSb	4	0·7	
B8	VSe	3	0·7	
B8	VTe	3	1·0	
B8	CrSe	4	3·7	p^3
B8	CrTe	4	3·6	p^3
B1	MnO	5	4·7	p^3
B1	MnS	5	5·0	p^3
B1	MnSe	5	4·9	p^3
B8	MnTe	5	5·1	p^3
B1	CoO	3	4·1	p^3
B8	CoS	3	1·0	
B8	NiS	2	0	

[8.12] and CrSb, MnSb, FeP and CoSb [8.13]. Let us calculate the number $2S_P$ deduced from Pearson's scheme, that is to say by supposing p^3 orbitals to be occupied; if the electronic formula of the isolated T atom is $d^x s^2$, the covalent formula of T V or T VI compounds will be $d^{x-1}(p^3) - (p^3)$ or $d^x(p^3) - (p^3)$ respectively, where the bonding electrons are shown in brackets. Thus $2S_P$ is equal to $x - 1$ (TV compounds) or x (T VI compounds) if $x - 1$ or $x \leqslant 5$, and to $11 - x$ (TV) or $10 - x$ (T VI) if $x - 1$ or $x > 5$ respectively. SUCHET [8.14] has noted that significant deviations occur for certain compounds and Fig. 8.5 shows that this deviation is usually of the order of two units. Thus TX compounds fall into two groups of which one (region 1) forms p^3 bonds and the other (region 2) some other sort of bond. We leave aside CoSb, for which the value of λ of -0.13 undoubtedly puts it amongst the metallic alloys, whatever its bond type.

To understand the significance of this observation we shall undertake, following ORGEL [8.15], an analysis of the role played by the d electrons in the hybrid bonding orbitals. We saw in Section 1.3 that there are five ψ_d

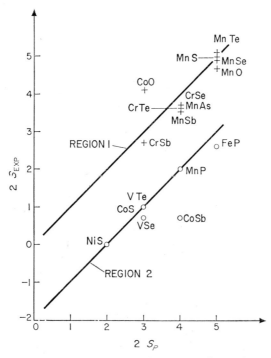

FIG. 8.5. Number of magnetons predicted according to Pearson and number found experimentally (following SUCHET [8.14])

orbitals; if one wishes to retain the independence of these various wave-functions, it is not possible to give them all an identical spatial form and one is led to introduce a different d_{z^2} orbital (Fig. 8.6). Let us suppose that the crystal contains spherical atoms X carrying at their centre some specific charge. Let us then try to find the effect on the T atom orbitals of the electrostatic field resulting in the direction of the co-ordinate axes from the charges carried by the six nearest neighbours to which it is bonded, neighbours that we shall call its **ligands**. The ligands lying along the z axis will evidently have an identical effect on the $d_{x^2-y^2}$ and d_{xy} orbitals but those situated along the x and y axes will have the greatest effect on the electrons occupying the $x^2 - y^2$ branches directed toward them rather than on those occupying the d_{xy} orbitals oriented along the bisectrices. Because of the symmetry, one finds in this way that the ligand field acts more strongly on the d_{z^2} orbital (which can be regarded as a linear combination of $d_{z^2-x^2}$ and of $d_{z^2-y^2}$, terms similar to $d_{x^2-y^2}$) than on the d_{xz} and d_{yz} orbitals. In an octahedral environment, the five d orbitals divide into two groups; in one group are the three d_{xy}, d_{xz} and d_{yz} orbitals, whose stability is little affected by the ligand field, and in the other group the two $d_{x^2-y^2}$ and d_{z^2} orbitals, which the field perturbs strongly. We shall designate these two

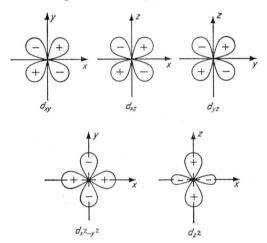

FIG. 8.6. The different ψ_d orbitals (following ORGEL [8.15])

groups by the notations $d\varepsilon$ and $d\gamma$ respectively, $d\gamma$ having the higher energy. Figure 1.1 shows that the levels follow one another in the order $4s$, $3d$ and $4p$, thus the $3d\gamma$ and $4p$ levels can become very close.

The structures of rocksalt and nickel arsenide are not typically metallic structures so that in their case we are forced to consider a bond of covalent character taking the form of trigonal pyramidal orbitals analogous to the p^3 orbitals. However, the metallic character of certain compounds such as NiAs, CoS or MnP leads us to consider the presence of free electrons in an incompletely filled level. Table 8.5, which gives a list of the principal hybrids, suggests d^2p orbitals and Fig. 8.7, which compares their behaviour with that for the p^3 orbitals for the two homologous compounds MnP and MnAs, shows that the choice of one or the other simply depends on a disorientation of the spins in the d level between the sub-levels $d\varepsilon$ and $d\gamma$. The observed difference of two units in the number of uncompensated spins $2S$ of the T atoms engaged in one or the other bond excludes all possibility of exchange between the d and p levels since these two units represent the spins of the two d level electrons which, if participating in iono-covalent bonds, would be compensated by the spins of their

TABLE 8.5

Type of bond	Orbitals used	Co-ordination c
Digonal linear	$\left\{\begin{matrix} s, p_z \\ d_{z^2}, p_z \end{matrix}\right\}$	2
Digonal rectangular	p_x, p_y	2
Trigonal plane	$\left\{\begin{matrix} s, p_x, p_y \\ s, d_{x^2-y^2}, d_{z^2} \\ d_{z^2}, p_x, p_y \end{matrix}\right\}$	3
Trigonal pyramidal	$\left\{\begin{matrix} p_x, p_y, p_z \\ d_{x^2-y^2}, d_{z^2}, p_z \end{matrix}\right\}$	3
Tetragonal plane	$\left\{\begin{matrix} d_{x^2-y^2}, s, p_x, p_y \\ d_{x^2-y^2}, d_{z^2}, p_x, p_y \end{matrix}\right\}$	4
Tetrahedral	$\left\{\begin{matrix} s, p_x, p_y, p_z \\ d_{xy}, d_{xz}, d_{yz}, s \end{matrix}\right\}$	4
Trigonal bipyramidal	$s, p_x, p_y, p_z, d_{z^2}$	5
Octahedral	$s, p_x, p_y, p_z, d_{x^2-y^2}, d_{z^2}$	6
Cubic	$s, p_x, p_y, p_z, d_{xy}, d_{xz}, d_{yz}, f_{xyz}$	8

partners from the metalloid. Thus we see that two electrons from the p level are free to participate in metallic conductivity. Their mutual compensation thus assumes a statistical character and this is why they are represented in Fig. 8.7 by a horizontal arrow, to show that they do not influence the other spins.

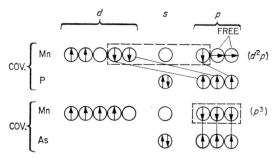

FIG. 8.7. Covalent aspect of the bonds in MnAs and MnP

We now know which types of bond the TX compounds having *B1*, *B8* and *B31* structures possess. Table 8.6 gives the respective values $2S$ for different T atoms in the two cases, and a knowledge of $2S_{\text{exp}}$ permits us to make an unambiguous choice. For the TX_2 compounds with *C6* and *C19* structures, we have a choice between the vacancy structure $(\square T)X_2$, derived

TABLE 8.6

	Compounds TX (B1, B8, B31)				Compounds TX$_2$ (C6, C19)			
	Orbital p^3	T V	T VI	Orbital d^2p	Orbital p^3	T VI$_2$	T VII$_2$	Orbital d^2sp^3
d^0	0	Sc	Ca	—	0	Ti	Ca	0
d^1	1	Ti	Sc	—	1	V	Sc	1
d^2	2	V	Ti	0	2	Cr	Ti	2
d^3	3	Cr	V	1	3	Mn	V	3
d^4	4	Mn	Cr	2	4	Fe	Cr	2
d^5	5	Fe	Mn	3	5	Co	Mn	1
d^6	4	Co	Fe	2	4	Ni	Fe	0
d^7	3	Ni	Co	1	3	Cu	Co	—
d^8	2	Cu	Ni	0	2	Zn	Ni	—
d^9	1	Zn	Cu	—	1	Ga	Cu	—
d^{10}	0	Ga	Zn	—	0	Ge	Zn	—

from TX and using the same p^3 bonds, and the formula TX$_2$, in which the T atom forms $d\gamma^2 sp^3$ orbital hybrids, with a consequent disorientation in the d level. One sees from the table that, for the first four compounds, these two bonds give the same value of $2S$ and so no choice can be made between them. If the disorientation of the spins results in a metallic conductivity for the TX compound, this will be just the reverse for the case of the TSe$_2$ and TTe$_2$ compounds, because the crystalline ionicity λ relative to the T–X bond is negative in the case of p^3 bonds and positive in the case of d^2sp^3 bonds. Finally, let us recall that for the TX$_2$ compounds having C2 and C18 structures, the values of $2S$ in the α (without disorientation) and β (with disorientation at d level) schemes have been given in the preceding section in Table 8.3.

Let now try to determine the limiting value of ligand field which is able to cause this disorientation at the d level. This field, within the frame-work of the crystallochemical model described in the preceding chapter, is evidently related to the effective charges q carried by the ligands, and hence to the polarity q/c of the bonds which the atom T forms with them. Figure 8.8 shows the polarity as a function of $2S_P$ for the TX compounds. The circles and crosses correspond to those of Fig. 8.5, and the compounds for which the magnetic criterion could not be used have been simply indicated with a point. One sees that the compounds from region 1 (p^3 orbitals) and 2 (d^2p orbitals) are arranged on either side of a boundary line. The parallel alignment of all the spins in the d level depends on their exchange interaction which is itself proportional to the number of $2S$ of these spins. It only gives way to a disorientation between $d\varepsilon$ and $d\gamma$ if the polarity (or if one wishes, the field) is sufficiently strong to destroy it; hence the linear nature of the boundary line [7.14]:

$$q/c = 2\,S_p \times 0{\cdot}22 - 0{\cdot}6$$

The only exceptions are those compounds in region 2 for which the sub-level $d\varepsilon$ is nearly full and where a high crystalline ionicity gives an electronic distribution much more like that of the ionic formula $d\varepsilon^5$ or

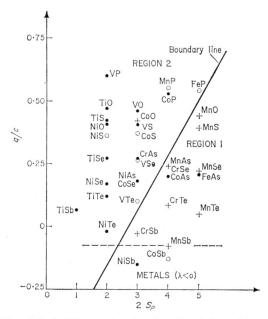

FIG. 8.8. Stability region for the p^3 and d^2p orbitals
(following SUCHET [8.14])

$d\varepsilon^6$ than that of the covalent formula $d\varepsilon^5(d\gamma^2p)$ or $d\varepsilon^6(d\gamma^2p)$. We saw in Section 8.1 that as far as an isolated ion was concerned, the formulae $d\varepsilon^5$ or $d\gamma^6$ would not be stable and the application of Hund's rules led to the formulae $d\varepsilon^3d\gamma^2$ or $d\varepsilon^4d\gamma^2$. One can suppose that this instability extends to an atom T which forms essentially ionic bonds, as in CoO and NiO ($\lambda = 0{\cdot}75$ and $0{\cdot}74$). The number of uncompensated spins found experimentally for CoO ($4{\cdot}1$) seems compatible, though a little large, with bonding by p^3 orbitals, particularly if the orbital moments are not completely quenched: it is in fact a semiconductor, as is NiO. On the other hand, CoSb and NiSb are situated in a region where the ionicity λ is clearly negative and are thus completely metallic.

In the case of the TX_2 compounds such a precise study is not possible. Only the p^3 orbitals appear to be used in the $C19$ structure, and the electrical and magnetic properties are too poorly known for the *C6* structure for one to be able to draw any reliable conclusions. For the *C2* and *C18* structures, one may note that the only three compounds to possess all their spins parallel in the *d* level (α scheme) have the maximum value of 2*S*, namely 5.

8.4 Extension of Weiss's Theory

In this section and the following, we shall restrict ourselves to the study of those TX and ($\square$T)X_2 compounds for which we concluded the existence of p^3 orbital bonds. The interpretation of the properties of these compounds is simpler than that for those where orbital hybrids intervene. The crystallochemical model described in the preceding chapter excludes *a priori* direct electronic coupling between the T atoms. Thus we shall study the indirect T–X–T interactions and shall always consider the iono-covalent T–X bond as a superposition of two electronic distributions, covalent and ionic, with probabilities $1 - \lambda$ and λ respectively.

For an ionic distribution, the metalloid X has completed its valence octet and acquired the electronic structure of the rare gas following it in the periodic classification, a structure which can be written symbolically as As^{3-}, S^{2-} or Br^- to indicate that the valence level contains six *p* electrons. The spins of these electrons compensate one another in pairs, so that the atom X is devoid of all magnetic moment and could not in any case serve to relay a direct magnetic interaction (Fig. 8.9). Let us now pass to the

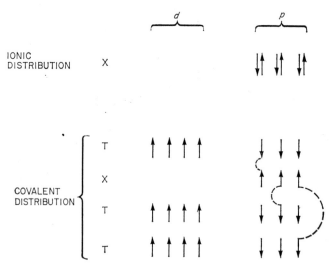

FIG 8 9. Spin orientations of the *d* and *p* levels in the ionic and covalent distributions (following SUCHET [8.16])

case of the covalent distribution where one supposes that the two electrons of each shared bond pair are distributed equally between the atoms present. Thus the metalloid X finds itself in a state which one can represent symbolically as As, S^+ or Br^{2+} to indicate that the valence level here contains only three p electrons, each of them engaged, moreover, in one bond pair to each of three T atoms (Fig. 8.9). The spins of these electrons are compensated on the scale of the elementary cell of the crystal, sometimes by the p electrons from a group of three neighbours situated on the superior triad, sometimes by the p electrons of a group of three neighbours situated on the inferior triad. Locally for the atom X, however, they are not compensated, and they contribute only 3/2 if one considers only a single group of three di-electronic bonds, as shown.

The theory of magnetic interactions proposed by Pierre Weiss in 1907 was based upon the parallel orientation of uncompensated spins by an **internal molecular field** H of poorly defined nature. Its application was thus originally restricted to crystals displaying a direct ferromagnetic interaction, almost the only ones, moreover, which had been studied at the turn of the century. Subsequently, it became clear that one must not attach the physical significance of a field to the quantity introduced by Weiss, and the work of Heisenberg gave a more precise specification of the nature of the electronic interaction energy which was responsible for this phenomenon. Nevertheless, even if one must only consider the field H as a fictitious field, the Weiss model retained all its value as a simple semi-empirical model. The interaction energy introduced by Heisenberg does not differ essentially from the energies occurring in the chemical bonds between identical atoms, for example in a crystal of germanium. SUCHET [8.16] has proposed to interpret the anti-parallel orientation of the spins of two electrons in the covalent bond pair with the aid of the Weiss field. The value of the interaction energy in Weiss's theory is $Jg\beta_m H$ where the vector J and the numbers g and β_m have the same significance as in Section 8.1. Here we shall take $g = 2$ and $J = S$. In the case considered in the preceding paragraph where $2S = 3/2$, the interaction energy thus has a value $(3/2)\beta_m H$ in the covalent scheme and zero in the ionic scheme, whilst taking into account their respective probabilities in the real crystal one would equate it to:

$$(3/2)\beta_m H(1 - \lambda)$$

One may recall that KRAMERS [8.17], considering the case of crystalline MnO, had already remarked that a purely ionic distribution $Mn^{2+}O^{2-}$ would not permit any explanation of the magnetic interaction, and had proposed a mechanism by which an electron was displaced in such a way as to be able to cause a paramagnetic moment for the oxygen atom. This electronic distribution, indicated symbolically as Mn^+O^-, was an *ad hoc* assumption, without any chemical justification. Much later ANDERSON [8.18] proposed to introduce covalent bonds using the *p* orbitals of the oxygen atom, but still retaining the same arbitary model Mn^+O^-, drawing no distinction between the covalent and ionic bond schemes. The point of view that we adopt here is on the contrary supported at once by the crystallographic structure, which requires consideration of the ideal covalent aspect of the bonds, as well as of the more familiar ionic aspect. In the covalent scheme the intervention of *p* orbitals is evidently only possible if each atom has three *p* electrons in its valence level, so as to engage them simultaneously in shared bonding pairs. This distribution is symbolized by

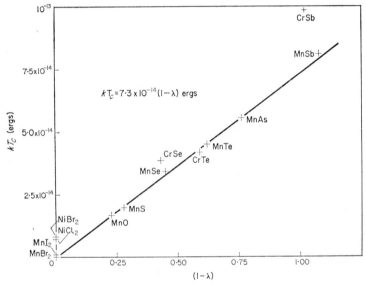

FIG. 8.10. Variation of the interaction energy with the probability of a covalent distribution (following SUCHET [8.16])

the formula Mn^-O^+. For Kramers' arbitrary model Mn^+O^-, we shall hence prefer to substitute the resonance hybrid:

$$(1 - \lambda)Mn^-O^+ + \lambda(Mn^{2+}O^{2-})$$

The coupling temperature T_c (the Curie or Néel point) of a transition element compound corresponds to the temperature at which the energy of thermal agitation kT balances that of the magnetic interactions, which we supposed to be equal to $(3/2)\beta_m H(1 - \lambda)$. We must therefore have a relationship between this temperature and the parameter λ:

$$kT_c = (3/2)\beta_m H(1 - \lambda).$$

This linear relationship, which is illustrated in Fig. 8.10, was discovered empirically [8.19] and then explained by the author [8.16]. Agreement with experiment is very good, and for the compounds of manganese in particular the numerical coefficient $(3/2)\beta_m H/k = 540°K$ allows the calculation of the Curie or Néel points of the crystals to within a few degrees from the values of λ (Table 8.7). Such a numerical coefficient corresponds to a value

TABLE 8.7

Compound	Interaction	Ionicity λ	calc. ← T_c°K → exptl.		Reference
MnSb	F	−0·08	583	587	Guillaud, *Thesis*, Strasbourg 1943
MnAs	F–AF?	0·24	410	403	(extrapolated) Guillaud ditto
MnTe	AF	0·38	335	325	Serre, *J. Phys. et Radium*, **8**, 146, 1947
MnSe	AF	0·55	243	247	Squire, *Phys. Rev.* **56**, 922, 1939
MnS	AF	0·72	151	140	ditto
MnO	AF	0·77	124	117	Squire, *C. R. Acad. Sci. Paris*, **207**, 449, 1938
MnI$_2$	AF	1	0	∼0	De Haas, *Physica*, **7**, 57, 1940
MnBr$_2$	AF	1	0	2	Wollan, *Phys. Rev.* **110**, 638, 1958
MnCl$_2$	AF	1	0	∼0	Trapneznikova, *Phys. Z. Sow. Union*, **11**, 55, 1937

of internal molecular field of the order of five million oersteds, that is to say virtually the value used by Weiss to explain the magnetism of iron.

The occurrence of compounds TX$_2$ with $1 - \lambda = 0$ is explained by the fact that they have a vacancy lattice, and that the interactions take place T–X–□–X–T passing via the vacancy □. This is at least what is shown by WOLLAN et al. [8.20] in a study made on the compound MnBr$_2$ at a temperature below T_c, that is to say below 2°K (Fig. 8.11). The bond □–X is necessarily fully ionic and the relationship above gives $T_c = 0$. The bond X–T is not entirely ionic, however, and the magnetic moment of the X atom can give rise to a weak interaction at two interatomic distances.

This excellent correlation leads us to consider the interactions in compounds bonded with p^3 orbitals as resulting simply from iono-covalent chemical bonds, the metalloid X having to resonate between its neighbours

T. Thus these interactions are not strictly related to the presence of un-paired electrons in the *d* level of the metallic atom, and they may occur equally in a compound such as CaS where the *d* level of calcium is empty

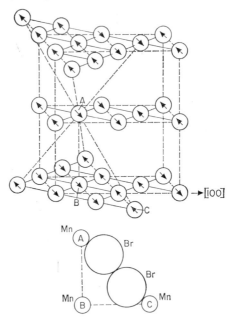

FIG. 8.11. Magnetic interactions in MnBr$_2$ (following WOLLAN *et al.* [8.20])

The role of the *d* electrons is to make these interactions observable via the intermediary of those physical properties particularly associated with the parallel or anti-parallel alignments of their spins.

8.5 Ferro or Antiferromagnetic Semiconductors

In Sections 8.3 and 8.4 we have been led to consider as semiconductors such compounds as MnAs and MnSb, which over a large temperature region exhibit a ferromagnetic interaction. HEIKES [8.21] has demonstrated a cor-relation between the electrical conductivity and the type of magnetic inter-actions and has supposed that there was a theoretical incompatibility between ferromagnetic interaction and semiconductivity. In fact, it is difficult for us to conceive how a hexa-co-ordinated compound TX forming bonds with p^3 orbitals and having a positively crystalline ionicity would have necessarily metallic properties as a result of ferromagnetic order. What are then the experimental criteria by which one recognizes a semi-conducting compound? Often one has a negligible Hall effect and carrier mobility, a thermo-electric power of between 5 and 20 microvolts/degree and a resistivity at ambient temperatures of the order of 10^{-3} to 10^{-4} ohm-cm. Such properties do not allow an infallible diagnosis and it is then necessary to fall back on the variation of resistivity as a function of temperature. If from some temperature, the temperature coefficient of resistivity becomes negative, one habitually considers that one is passing from the region where semiconductivity is determined by the mechanisms described in Chapter 2 and entering the region of **intrinsic** semiconductivity, governed by the mechanism of bond-breaking described in Section 6.1.

Figures 8.12 and 8.13 show the variation of resistivities of MnAs and MnSb crystals, according to the work of FISCHER and PEARSON [8.22]. MnAs shows the peculiarity of having a Curie point near 310°K and a

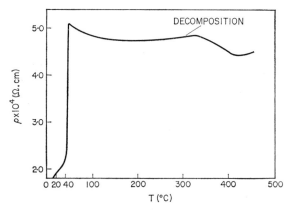

FIG. 8.12. Resistivity of MnAs as a function of temperature (following FISCHER et al. [8.22])

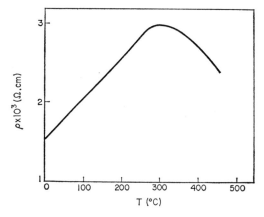

FIG. 8.13. Resistivity of MnSb as a function of temperature (following FISCHER et al. [8.22])

second transition point, perhaps a Néel point, at 403°K. The negative temperature coefficient between these two points, that is to say in the region presumed to be antiferromagnetic, is extremely clear. MnSb also shows a negative temperature coefficient appearing in the neighbourhood of the coupling temperature. The same phenomenon has been observed by SUZUOKA [8.23] for the antiferromagnetic compound CrSb whose Néel point is at 718°K, and by UCHIDA et al. [8.24] for the antiferromagnetic compound MnTe. In the perovskite structure, VOLGER [8.25] described the same behaviour for the ferromagnetic compound $La_{0.8}Sr_{0.2}MnO_3$ and HEIKES [8.26] has recently found it in the related compound $La_{0.7}Ca_{0.3}MnO_3$. Thus it is not related to the passage from extrinsic to intrinsic semiconductivity, but rather with a phenomenon related to the coupling temperature.

The spins of the unpaired electrons are ordered in the coupling region and are disordered in the paramagnetic region. The phenomenon described above is thus most certainly related to the scattering of the electrons by the disordered spins above the temperature T_c. A scattering of this sort is well known for metallic alloys; see the study by COLES [8.27]. If at low temperatures the effects of impurities are ignored, the resistivity splits into two terms:

$$\rho = \rho_{atom} + \rho_{spin}$$

The first term in this sum, arising from the thermal agitation of the atoms, is responsible for the classical law of the form $(1 + \alpha t)$. The second term, arising from the disorder of the spins, is zero at low temperatures, displays a strong positive temperature coefficient immediately below T_c, and then in the paramagnetic domain takes a value calculated by FRIEDEL and DE GENNES [8.28] which we simplify as:

$$\rho_{spin} = KS(S + 1)/N$$

where K summarizes the influence of several temperature independent factors, and N is the number of free electrons or, more generally, the number of free charge carriers. Figure 8.14 gives the contributions of the two terms in the case of iron [8.29].

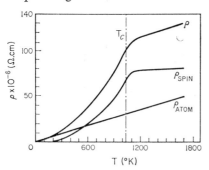

FIG. 8.14. Contributions to the resistivity of iron from the thermal agitation of the atoms and from the disordered spins (following WEISS et al. [8.29])

In the case of semiconducting compounds there is no doubt that both the above terms occur, but in general their variation remains small compared with the exponential variation of the principal term:

$$\rho = \rho_0 \exp (E_G/2kT)$$

However, let us suppose that E_G is very small and S large; it may happen that the positive temperature coefficient of the term ρ_{spin} outweighs the negative coefficient from the exponential so that an intrinsic semiconductor will be able to display an apparent metallic behaviour at temperatures immediately below T_c and show a resistivity maximum for $T = T_c$. Figure 8.15 gives the possible combination of the two contributions in the case of MnTe.* Note that ρ_{spin} is not a constant here for $T > T_c$ because of the variation in N. Finally, let us remark that the semiconducting character of such compounds can only be identified for temperatures at least equal to T_c. The condition $\lambda \geqslant 0$ mentioned in Section 7.2 must hence, in all rigour, be applied at the temperature T_c and not at ambient temperatures. Now

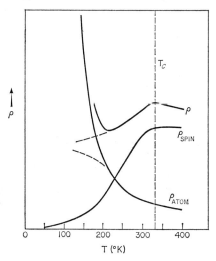

FIG. 8.15. Probable contributions to the resistivity in MnTe
(following SUCHET [8.2])

in the calculation of λ, the Pauling ionic radii determined from the inter-atomic distances are introduced and will increase at the same time as the crystal expands. Thus the condition $\lambda \geqslant 0$ at T_c corresponds at ambient temperatures to a condition $\lambda \geqslant -0.05$ approx., which allows us to consider as semiconductors CrSb (-0.03) and MnSb (-0.08).

The above interpretation, which has been put forward several times by SUCHET [8.2], [8.16], was confirmed by the discovery by BUSCH et al. [8.30] of ferromagnetic semiconducting compounds for which the temperature coefficient of resistivity is negative. The latter study concerned the chalco-genides of europium, crystallizing in the rocksalt structure, whose Curie

---

* The situation is more complicated for MnAs, MnSb, CrSb and CrTe, whose metallic state below T_c results from interactions between d electrons and free carriers; see IRKHIN and TUROV, *Fiz. Met. Metallov.* **4,** 9, 1957.

points are in the region of 10 to 20°K. The number of unpaired electrons here is high ($2S = 7$ against 4 for MnSb and 3 for CrSb), but the activation energy is relatively very high (1·6 eV for EuSe as against some tenths only for CrSb, MnAs and MnSb).

Finally, let us try to understand what differentiates ferromagnetism and antiferromagnetism in a semiconductor. Since the orientation of the un-compensated spins in the d level of the atom T is governed by that of the spins of the bonding electrons in the p level of the metalloid X, the behaviour of the latter electrons is of the greatest importance. The concept of the trigonal resonant bond set out in Section 2.5 supposes in fact that this bond may be established equally well by one or other branch of the p orbital function in a given direction. In the case of ferromagnetism the orientation of the spins in the d and p levels of the atom are shown schematically in Fig. 8.16. We see that the same p electron of the metalloid

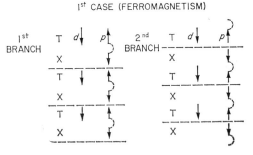

FIG. 8.16. Spin orientation in the two branches of a p orbital in the case of ferromagnetic interaction (following SUCHET [8.31])

can form the bond with the two branches of the orbital since its spin retains the same orientation when we pass from one branch to the other. On the contrary, in the case of antiferromagnetism, shown schematically in Fig. 8.17, the orientation of the spin of this electron is modified from one

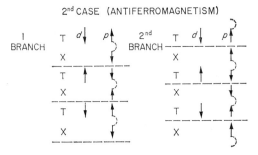

FIG. 8.17. Spin orientation in the two branches of a p orbital for the case of antiferromagnetic interaction (following SUCHET [8.31])

branch to the other, or, more reasonably, the bond can no longer be established by the same electron. However, in order that one should have the right to envisage the presence of a second electron with an opposed spin on the atom X, it follows that one must have an electronic distribution corresponding to an ionic bond, or at the very least a large probability λ for such a distribution [8.31] (cf. Fig. 7.1).

Table 8.8 classifies the different semiconducting compounds TX considered previously, as a function of their type of interaction and their

TABLE 8.8

$2S = 2$	NiO	$\lambda =$	0·74	AF	2nd order
$2S = 3$	CrSb		−0·03	AF	1st order
	CoO		0·75	AF	2nd order
$2S = 4$	MnSb		−0·08	F	
	MnAs		0·24	F	
	CrTe		0·41	F	
	CrSe		0·57	AF	3rd order?
$2S = 5$	MnTe		0·38	AF	1st order
	MnSe		0·55	AF	
	MnS		0·72	AF	2nd order
	MnO		0·77	AF	2nd order

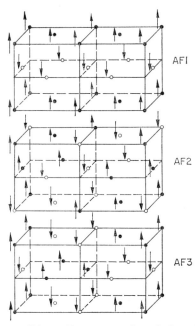

FIG. 8.18. Various possible antiferromagnetic orderings in the *B1* structure (following SMART [8.33])

ionicity λ. We have included in this table the ferromagnetic compound CrTe, although its semiconducting character cannot be observed because of the presence, as in the case of CoTe, of a metallic phase [8.32]. One sees that the condition $\lambda > 0\cdot5$ for antiferromagnetism is obeyed for $2S = 4$. For the other entries, let us recall that in fact first order antiferromagnetism results from indirect ferromagnetic interactions [8.33], as shown in Fig. 8.18, and that the nickel-arsenide structure in which CrSb and MnTe crystallize possesses just the privileged planes needed for such interactions with respect to the rocksalt structure [8.13].

In the case of the TX_2 compounds crystallizing in the $C19$ structure with the same p^3 bonds, the existence of T–X–□–X–T interactions, through the intermediary of a □–X bond of ionicity 1 mentioned in the preceding section, leads to the forecast of antiferromagnetism in agreement with experiment. Although we have in principle excluded from this section bonds formed by means of s-p orbital hybrids, let us note that the four bonding electrons of the metalloid have their spins parallel in the TX_2 compounds crystallizing in the $C2$ and $C18$ structures. Thus the situation is analogous to the one which we have been considering, and the existence of antiferromagnetic interactions again supposes a high value for the probability λ. One knows that $MnTe_2$ ($\lambda = 0\cdot7$) and MnS_2 ($\lambda = 0\cdot9$) are known to be of the type $AF1$ and $AF3$ respectively [8.34].

One of the consequences of the above rule is that one has little chance of discovering ferrimagnetic semiconductors having high carrier mobilities, since the acoustic scattering increases rapidly with λ (cf. Section 7.4).

N.B. Magnetic interactions have been treated in a more physical way by J. B. GOODENOUGH in *Magnetism and the Chemical Bond*, Interscience, New York (1963). Although there are some discrepancies, this approach and ours are not contradictory and the parameter R_c of this author could probably be related to the ionicity λ.

Chapter 9

ORGANIC SEMICONDUCTORS

9.1 Organic Molecular Crystals

IN the inorganic field there are semiconducting crystals where the iono-covalent bonds are restricted to molecular dimensions, such as AsI_3, SnI_4, Sb_2S_3. In this case semiconductivity must involve the jumping of charged carriers from one molecule to the other, either by means of a bond resonance which momentarily reunites the atoms of two neighbouring molecules, or by some other mechanism. This is the general rule for organic semiconductors, which for several years now have created growing interest. Their resistivity is high, usually greater than a megohm-cm, and the absence of any electrolytic transport of charge has been demonstrated by the classical experiment of RIEHL [9.1] on liquid naphthalene. (No polarization effects could be detected after the passage of a current of 0·5 micro-amperes over a period of seven consecutive days.)

The first mention of photoconductivity in an organic solid (anthracene) appears to be due to POCCHETTINO [9.2] in 1906. The principal advances in the study of organic semiconductors were made following the discovery by VARTANYAN [9.3] of the photoconductivity of organic dyes and of their role in increasing the sensitivity of photographic emulsions; the discovery of the conductivity of the phthalocyanines and their metallic derivatives by ELEY [9.4] and VARTANYAN [9.5]; then the systematic studies of METTE and PICK [9.6] and INOKUCHI [9.7] on anthracene and those of PICK and WISSMAN [9.8] on naphthalene. Figure 9.1 shows the schematic diagrams for some of the molecules studied all of which are of aromatic type.

The substances used have usually been purified by crystallization or sublimation, and the measurements made upon powders compressed between two metallic electrodes or upon films deposited by condensation between two metallic deposits. However, present-day studies often employ single crystals and can be used to give the variation of conductivity (in darkness) with temperature along the various crystallographic axes. The law followed is the usual one for semiconductors:

$$\sigma = \sigma_0 \exp\left(-E_G/2kT\right)$$

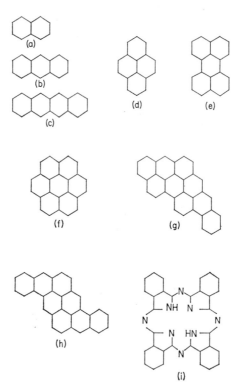

FIG. 9.1. (*a*) naphthalene, (*b*) anthracene, (*c*) tetracene (phenacene), (*d*) pyrene, (*e*) perylene, (*f*) coronene, (*g*) violanthrene, (*h*) pyranthrene, (*i*) phthalocyanine

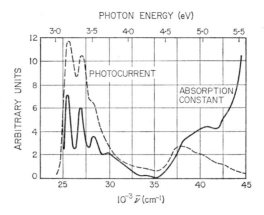

FIG. 9.2. Absorption and photoconduction spectra for anthracene
(following BREE *et al.* [9.9])

where the factor 2 in the exponential supposes intrinsic conductivity (cf. Section 6.1). The optical absorption spectrum, which generally parallels the photoconductivity spectrum (Fig. 9.2, according to [9.9]), allows one to determine a value $E_{G_{ph}}$ for the photo-chemical energy gap which is often much greater than the preceding one, E_G. Ohm's law is no longer obeyed for fields greater than 1000 volts/cm, but breakdown of the crystal usually only occurs for fields around 10^6 V/cm. The mobilities are very small.

One important observation is that the sign of the majority charge carriers is usually positive. This may be concluded from both the study of the thermo-electric effect in these substances and from the direction of conduction for a diode made between them and a metal point. It can be deduced from observations of the operation of photoconductive cells made by pressing the molten semiconductor between two glass plates covered with conducting tin oxide and leaving the system to freeze [9.10]. The photocurrent furnished by such 'sandwiched' cells is always much greater when the illuminated electrode is positive (Fig. 9.3).

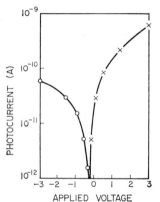

FIG. 9.3. Photocurrent in anthracene as a function of applied voltage (following NORTHROP *et al.* [9.10])

The phenomenon of luminescence (cf. Curie [9.11]) occurs very frequently in organic semiconductors. Whilst photoconductivity results from the increase in the number of carriers due to the creation of electron-hole pairs by the photoelectric effect, luminescence can result from the recombination of these two types of carrier. Thus the two phenomena are in some senses contradictory, since a significant luminescence generally accompanies a rapid recombination, whilst a significant photocurrent can only be established if the lifetime of the carriers is sufficient, i.e. if the recombination is sufficiently slow. Nevertheless, they are often encountered in the same substance. This apparent incompatibility disappears in the case where the luminescence is associated with the capture of one type of carrier and the photoconductivity associated with the other type (cf. [7]).

Table 9.1 gives some values for σ_0 and E_G for the principal solids studied. The data is supplied by different authors, so that comparison is not easy. E_G is often obtained by means of measurements on powders, and $E_{G_{ph}}$ by means of measurements on films. The results of measurements made on single crystals are indicated with an asterisk. The order of magnitude only has been indicated for log σ_0. One may refer, for greater precision, to the

TABLE 9.1

Class	Substance	$\text{Log } \sigma_0$ $(\Omega^{-1} \text{cm}^{-1})$	E_G (eV)	E_{Gph} (eV)
Polyacenes	Naphthalene	−5	1·4*[1]	
	Anthracene	−3	1·8 1·6–2·7*	3·0
	Tetracene	−1	1·7	3·6*
	Pentacene	−2	1·5	
	Pyrene	−3	2·0	3·2*
	Perylene	−1	2·0	
	Coronene	+1	2·3	
	Ovalene	−6	1·1	1·2
	Violanthrene	−7	0·8	0·9
	Isoviolanthrene	−7	0·8	0·85
	Pyranthrene	−7	1·1	0·85
Poly-ketones	Violanthrone	−3	0·8	0·8
	Isoviolanthrone	−3	0·8	0·9
	Pyranthrone	−7	1·1	1·1
Azo-aromatics	Flaventhrone	−5	0·7	0·8
	Indanthrone	−10	0·6	0·7
	Indanthrazine	−10	0·7	0·8
Phthalocyanines	Phthalocyanine	−4 (+1)*	1·5[2] 1·8*	1·6
	„ Cu	−4 (+2)*	2·1 1·8*	
	„ Ni		1·5*	
	„ Co		1·6*	

[1] After 9.1   [2] After 9.12

work of GARRETT (cf. [6]). The values of the energy gap contained in this table call for some remarks. For the simple polyacenes (chains of rings), if we disregard the first member (naphthalene), we see that E_G decreases regularly –1·8–1·7–1·5– as the number of rings increases –3 (anthracene), 4 (tetracene), 5 (pentacene). Similarly for the more complex polyacenes, we find that the greatest energy gaps characterize compact molecules such as coronene, whilst E_G falls below unity for violanthrene and isoviolanthrene, where the number of rings is three times as great along the length of the molecules as across its width. There is thus a distinct shape factor.

9.2 Double Bonds and π Electrons

In Section 1.3 the different types of orbital which could be used in the bond between two atoms were considered, but it has so far been supposed that this bond requires no more than the introduction of two electrons (one in the case of resonance). Such a bond is said to be simple, but inorganic chemistry, and above all organic chemistry, offers many examples of **double bonds** where each atom has two unpaired electrons to share with its partner. The two bonds cannot be equivalent; if, for example, the first is formed by the mutual sharing of two unpaired p_y electrons, and if there are also two unpaired p_z electrons, the latter will be disposed perpendicularly to the axis of the first bond, and thus can link up only outside the electron cloud corresponding to the first bond (Fig. 9.4).

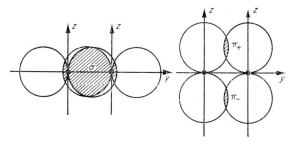

FIG. 9.4. σ and π bonds in a diatomic molecule

Those electrons taking part in a simple bond possessing rotational symmetry about the bond axis are called σ **electrons** and those which are engaged in the second bond of a double bond, and do not possess this symmetry, π **electrons**. It is in organic chemistry where the π electrons play the most important role, in chains or rings of carbon atoms. Figure 9.5 shows the mode of bonding for CH groups comprising **conjugated double**

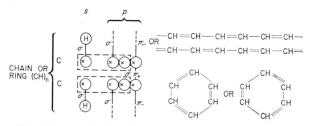

FIG. 9.5. σ and π bonds in the polyenes and polyacenes

bonds in a chain (polyene) or in rings (benzene). The direction of a p orbital does not display any privileged sense, the bonds with π electrons can be made to either one or the other neighbour with complete indifference, and are represented in these two cases by π_+, π_-. Thus one obtains an **electronic**

delocalization which in graphite, for instance, which is made up of superimposed networks of such hexagons (Fig. 4.5), leads to metallic conductivity. LONDON [9.13] showed that the diamagnetism of the benzene ring revealed the existence of an electronic conductivity in the presence of magnetic field, and that the benzene molecule must be considered, in the absence of a dissipative mechanism, as a superconductor. On the same basis a chain of conjugated double bonds would display metallic conductivity if it were possible to attach electrodes to each of its ends.

The preceding considerations have an important consequence; that the mechanism for semiconductivity can only be intermolecular, and can only involve the transfer of charge from molecule to molecule. The shape factor noted in the preceding section can perhaps thus be explained by the larger number of transfers 'in parallel' possible in the case of elongated molecules. For the rest one falls back on a model of conducting grains (molecules) with resistive boundaries analogous to those considered in Section 5.3, and hence to a large loss angle [9.12]. We saw that recent results on a large number of organic semiconductors showed the existence of positively charged majority carriers, so that π electrons could not play a direct role in this transfer. Nonetheless, this was still the opinion which prevailed for a long time, and SZENT-GYÖRGYI [9.14] suggested in 1941 that the transfer of such electrons could play an important role in the fundamental physical processes of living organisms. Moreover, the biological importance of this mechanism of semiconduction has been amply confirmed by the work of ELEY [9.4] on the phthalocyanines, and the discovery by NELSON [9.15] of the semiconductivity of chlorophyll throws a new light on the phenomenon of photosynthesis.

In any case, one could consider relating E_G to the number of π electrons existing in each molecule and INOKUCHI [9.16] showed, for a series of eleven polycyclic compounds, that the conductivity increased and the energy gap decreased when the number of π electrons increased. A simple model for the mechanism of intermolecular semiconductivity was given a few years later by ELEY and PARFITT [9.12] and we shall now discuss it. Figure 9.6, following ELEY [9.17], represents three aromatic molecules, of benzene for example, side by side in the crystal and, on the second line, their corresponding potential wells. There are n orbitals or molecular levels common to the n π-electrons of each molecule and the latter initially fill the $n/2$ lower levels (molecule on the left). If an electron receives an energy (activation energy) of E_G allowing it to pass from the level $n/2$ to the level $(n/2) + 1$ (centre molecule, plain arrow), charge transfer becomes possible (dashed arrow) either toward the molecule on the left (hole from the level $n/2$), or toward that on the right (electron from the $(n/2) + 1$ level). Such a transfer from one potential well to another, the carrier having insufficient energy to allow it to cross the potential barrier existing between the two molecules, can be considered by analogy with known phenomena, notably the behaviour of p–n junctions in covalent crystals. One gives to this phenomenon the name **tunnel effect.** The experimental fact that the majority

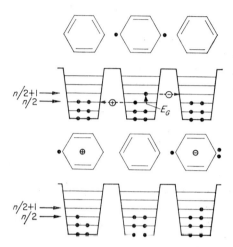

FIG. 9.6. Mechanism of intermolecular semiconductivity
(following ELEY [9.11])

carriers are positively charged draws our attention to the transfer by tunnel effect of a hole to the $n/2$ level.

ELEY *et al.* [9.18], [9.12] calculated the activation energy necessary for these transfers by using a simple mathematical treatment and found the

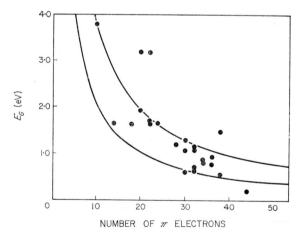

FIG. 9.7. Relationship between E_G and number of π electrons
(following ELEY *et al.* [9.12])

following two relations, the first applicable to open chains, and the second for closed rings:

$$E_G = [h^2/8md^2][(n + 1)/n^2]$$

$$E_G = [h^2/4md^2][1/n]$$

where d is the length of the carbon–carbon bond in aromatic compounds (1·39 Å), m the mass of the electron and h Planck's constant. Figure 9.7 shows how the experimental results lie in relation to the theoretical curves. This theory predicts zero activation energy for a free radical possessing an unpaired electron in the $[(n/2) + 1]$ level and is confirmed by the small value (0·26 eV) found experimentally for $\alpha : \alpha$—diphenyl β—picrylhydrazyl.

9.3 Charge Transfer Complexes

The idea of a compensated lattice which has been introduced in Section 3.5 has a particular pertinence to the field of organic semiconductors where a large number of recently prepared compounds can be written in the form $[R]^-M^+$ or $[R]^+X^-$, where M and X are general representations for the alkali metals and halogens respectively, and possibly even for simple radicals with pronounced electronegative or electropositive character. This important field was opened in 1954 by HOLMES-WALKER and UBBELOHDE [9.19] who prepared anthracene-alkali compounds $[An]^{x-}M_x^+$ with x lying between one and two. These authors were investigating the properties of condensed aromatic nuclei much smaller than those of graphite (C–C distance of 1·39 Å rather than 1·42). The previous work of McDONNELL et al. [9.20] on the addition compounds C_8K and C_8Br had shown that the planar layers of condensed aromatic nuclei in graphite were capable of accepting electrons from the potassium atoms, or of donating or losing them to the bromine atoms, giving these two cases pseudo-metallic structures where the electrical and thermal conductivities of graphite were considerably enhanced.

Holmes-Walker and Ubbelohde showed that there was a considerable decrease of volume (16% in the case of $[An]^{2-}Na_2^+$) upon the formation of the anthracene complexes which excluded the possibility of a simple dispersion of neutral atoms. The activation energy varied little, falling from 2·7 eV (for easy direction of conductivity) to 2·5 or 2·4 eV according to the proportion of sodium, but the resistivity at ambient temperatures diminished considerably, and fell to around 10 megohms-cm. At the same time, the diamagnetism due to the π-electrons of anthracene gives way to paramagnetism for $[An]^-Na^+$, an effect which is further accentuated for $[An]^{2-}Na_2^+$, revealing the existence of unpaired electrons not engaged in the double bonds. These authors envisaged the appearance of free radicals such as mono or disodium-anthracene and mentioned the analogy between solid alkali-hydrocarbon 'solutions' and alkali-ammoniac liquids.

At more or less the same time, AKAMATU *et al.* [9.21] prepared analogous complexes $[R]^{x+}X_x^-$ such as perylenebromine, where the polycyclic hydrocarbon now donates rather than accepts an electron. The activation energies are very much lower than in the preceding case and of the order of 0·1 to 0·2 eV. The very low resistivities of these materials, of the order of a few ohm-cm, are not always stable and may rise to 1000 ohm-cm or more after several weeks. This instability arises from the existence of a slow substitution reaction for the halogen, the hydrocarbon–halogen complex with small resistivity evolving towards a halogenated hydrocarbon of high resistivity of the type considered in Section 9.1. When this reaction cannot occur, as in the case of the violanthrene–iodide complex, the electrical properties are stable. SLOUGH and UBBELOHDE [9.23], starting from the known fact that the introduction of a nitrogen atom in the ring facilitates the incorporation of an acceptor (addition complexes are obtained more easily with pyridine than with benzene) prepared analogous compounds starting from various benzoquinolines and found similar results. ELEY and INOKUCHI [9.24] also used nitrogen compounds but replaced the halogen X by chloranil, bromanil or iodanil. More recently, other complexes of the same type have been prepared by LABES *et al.* [9.25] (cf. Table 9.2).

TABLE 9.2

Compound AB	Ratio A/B	$\rho\Omega$ cm at 25°C	E_G (eV)
p-Phenylenediamine-chloranil	3/2	10^7	1·32
Diaminodurene-chloranil	1/1	10^4	0·58
3–8 Diaminopyrene-chloranil	1/1	10^3	0·3
3–10 Diaminopyrene-chloranil	3/1	10^6	0·8
3–8 Diaminopyrene-bromanil	1/1	10^3	0·3
3–8 Diaminopyrene-iodanil	1/1	10^6	0·82
Perylene-iodide	1/3	2 to 3	0·03
Coronene-iodide	1/1	10^8	1·0

GARRETT [9.26] considered these charge-transfer complexes (or organic compensated lattices) as constituting a different class of semiconductors from that described in Section 9.1, and this distinction is certainly justified by their low resistivity. However, it is not certain if the mechanism of semiconductivity here differs so much from the one which we have discussed in the preceding section. If we refer again to the model due to Eley, we see that we should have to have zero activation energy for $[An]^-$, as for a free radical (Fig. 9.8*a*) to justify the hypothesis of conduction by tunnelling of electrons from the $(n/2 + 1)$ level. In fact, since E_G is here of the same order as for An, one can deduce from this that only conduction by tunnelling of the holes is possible (*b*). In the case of [An]$^+$ on the contrary, it has to be supposed that the conduction occurs by electron tunnelling (*c*), to take account of the small activation energies observed. It is necessary to note the remarkable influence which the presence of interstitial ions appear to have on the pre-exponential term σ_0, confirming the importance of the intermolecular barriers in organic semiconductors. This effect might be related to the change from an even to an odd number of π electrons, one electron now having been transferred to the anion or from the cation.

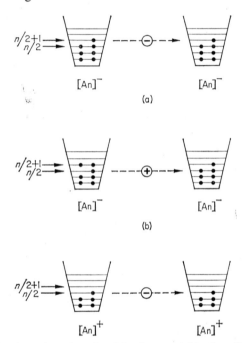

FIG. 9.8. Mechanism of semiconductivity for partial lattices [An]$^-$ and [An]$^+$

9.4 Plastic Materials

The idea that a molecule with conjugated double bonds (such as we discussed in Section 9.2) could have a metallic conductivity, has given rise to a number of studies directed toward obtaining conducting or semiconducting plastic materials possessing chains of conjugated double bonds. For example, it is possible to remove HBr from polyvinyl bromide

$$\ldots -CH_2-CHBr-CH_2-CHBr- \ldots$$

in order to prepare polyvinylene

$$\ldots -CH=CH-CH=CH- \ldots$$

which, in the form of a film, displays a large electrical and optical aniso-
tropy and a very low resistivity. The formation of double bonds can often
be obtained simply by heating a saturated chain, thus polystyrene:

$$\ldots -CH(C_6H_5)-CH_2-CH(C_6H_5)-CH_2- \ldots$$

gives a conducting three-dimensional lattice. The fall in resistivity is
accompanied by a coloration of the material. An initially colourless
product becomes absorbing in the far ultra-violet for a sequence of three
double bonds, yellow with absorption around 3·5 microns for a sequence
of four double bonds, red for eight or nine and black for twenty or more.
Finally, in the most recent techniques, irradiation by gamma-rays from
cobalt, or by electron or neutron beams, also enhances the conductivity.

WINSLOW et al. [9.27] studied the variations of resistivity as a function
of the temperature to which various polymers were heated, and attempted
to interpret the mechanism of pyrolysis. Figure 9.9 represents the variation

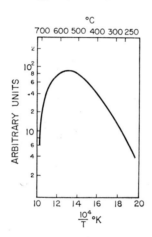

FIG. 9.9. Paramagnetic resonance in divinylbenzene after pyrolysis
(following WINSLOW et al. [9.27])

of the paramagnetic resonance absorption in pre-oxidized polydivinyl-
benzene. It shows that the concentration of unpaired electrons increases
rapidly at about 600°C, but diminishes at still higher temperatures. These
authors suppose that pyrolysis, at temperatures greater than 700°C, produces a material whose structure approaches more and more that of
graphite, with the loss of hydrogen, oxygen and aliphatic radicals. Figure
9.10 shows this evolution schematically for a co-polymer of divinylbenzene
and ethylvinylbenzene.

Important progress was made toward the end of 1959 by Nobel
prize-winner N. Semyonov. The products obtained by the irradiation of

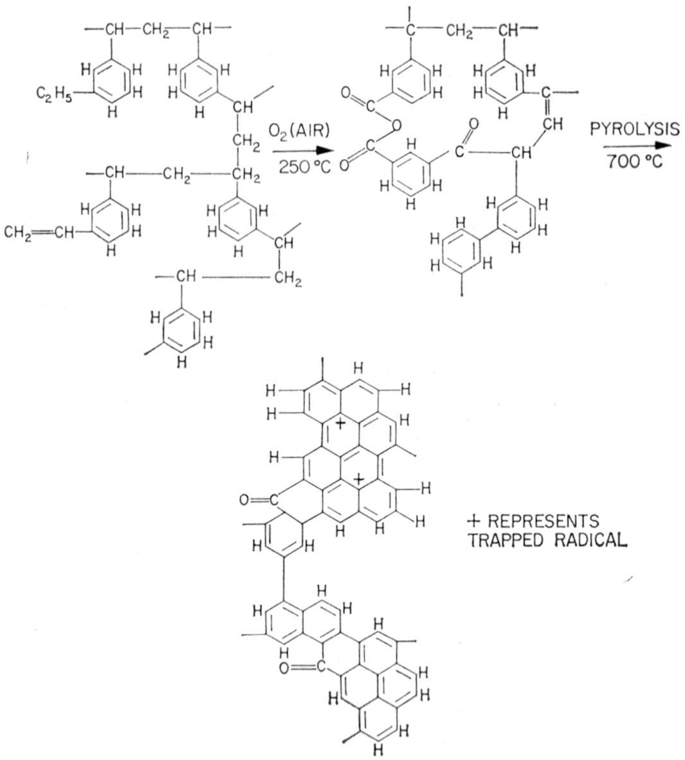

FIG. 9.10. Pyrolysis of a divinylbenzene/ethylvinylbenzene co-polymer
(following WINSLOW *et al.* [9.27])

polyacrylonitrile-siloxane co-polymers were stable and showed a rather
high electrical conductivity.

TOPTCHIEV *et al.* [9.28] showed that the thermal treatment of poly-
acrylonitrile could create conjugated double bonds in the chain by
cyclization, and then de-hydrogenation by oxidation (Fig. 9.11). Thus
electron paramagnetic resonance reveals the presence of 10^{18} to 10^{19} unpaired electrons per gramme of material, and in certain circumstances one
can obtain a semiconductor which is stable up to about 300°C, whose
activation energy is 1·7 eV and whose resistivity at room temperatures is

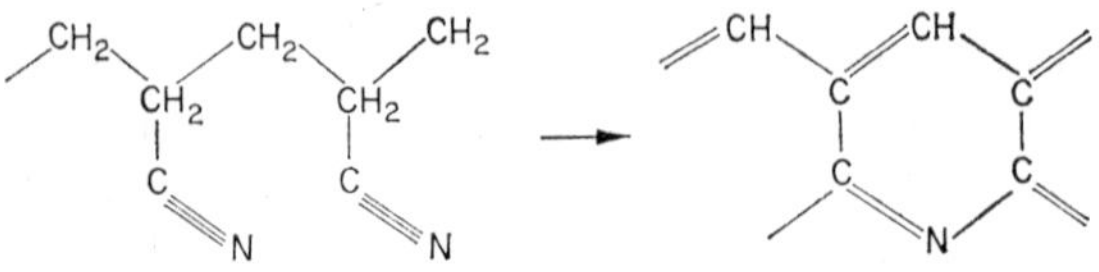

FIG. 9.11. Appearance of conjugated double bonds in polyacronitrile
(following TOPTCHIEV *et al.* [9.28])

very high. This polymer swells in concentrated salt solutions and these authors have shown that the incorporation of $CuCl_2$ allows the resistivity at 300°C to be reduced to 100Ω cm at room temperatures. They did not state what effect this had on the activation energy. It is possible, in our opinion, that the ions Cu^{2+} and Cl^- reduce the pre-exponential term σ in the same way as the alkali ions M^+ or halogen ions X^- do in the case of the cyclic compounds (anthracene-sodium, perylene-bromine, etc. . . .), by modifying the parity of the π electrons and so decreasing the molecular barriers between the chains.

The field of semiconducting plastic materials is probably one of the most promising branches of organic chemistry, and research will certainly become intensified in the next few years.

N.B. New compounds have been recently reported, notably tetracyano-p-benzo quinodimethane (TCNQ) ion-radical salts (see R. G. KEPLER *et al. Phys. Rev. Letters* **5,** 503 (1960) and D. S. ACKER *et al. J. Amer. Chem. Soc.* **82,** 6408 (1960)). Although their conductivity can be much greater than those discussed above (0·01Ω cm), they too may be considered as charge transfer complexes $M^+(TCNQ)_x^-$ with $x = 1-1\cdot5-2-$, etc.

Organic Semiconductors by Y. OKAMOTO and W. BRENNER, Reinhold, New York (1964), gives a more detailed review of the field summarized in this chapter.

CONCLUSION

SEMICONDUCTIVITY is not the exclusive property of a small group of chemical compounds which are to be looked upon as laboratory curiosities. It is a very widespread phenomenon and is of interest to chemists because of the new point of view which is provided by the study of electrical conductivity.

The various research laboratories of the world are vying with one another in their attempts to discover and patent the applications of new compounds showing properties superior to those of known materials. WERNICK [10] remarked recently that if one could find a semiconducting compound having the mobility of InSb (80,000 cm^2/Vs), the thermal conductivity of AgSbTe$_2$ (6 mW/cm °C), and the energy gap of SiC (2·8 eV), it would be possible to make thermo-electric generators with efficiencies of 50%, as compared with Diesel generators whose efficiencies are around 40%. Although such a combination of properties is extremely unlikely, this example demonstrates clearly the important practical consequences which such studies could have. The situation is similar in the case of the transition element compounds. The discovery of a ferromagnetic semiconductor having an appreciable carrier mobility would completely change the current outlook on magneto-electric devices.

We hope that we have given some basic ideas, in part original, which will allow research groups to enter into this competition.

174

APPENDIX

Band Theory

WE have defined the energy gap, Section 6.1, as that energy which, transferred to a bonding electron, frees it and leaves a hole in its place. As an example we considered the excitation of $3p$ electron to a higher level in silicon. In fact, this simplified model is not truly applicable to a crystal where the energy levels of the different atoms are smeared out. Thus we speak of valence (bound electrons) or conduction (free electrons) bands.

We arrive at this picture by considering the conditions under which a beam of electrons can move within a crystal. The energy of a free electron is purely kinetic and may be expressed simply as a function of the wave number of the associated wave, using the fundamental relationship $mv = h\mathbf{k}$:

$$E = mv^2/2 = (h^2/2m)\mathbf{k}^2$$

An energy of 1 eV thus corresponds to $\mathbf{k} = 0{\cdot}815.10^{-7}$ cm^{-1} and $\lambda = 12{\cdot}3$Å, for the associated wave. The function $E(\mathbf{k})$ is a parabola with axis $\mathbf{k} = 0$ when the electron moves in a uniform potential. When the latter is replaced by a periodic potential such as that always found within a crystal, the wave-like nature of the electron allows us to foresee that certain particle energies, corresponding to certain wavelengths of the associated function, can be forbidden in particular directions of propagation. For example, it is well known that an X-ray beam is not completely transmitted by a crystal, but that all the wavelengths satisfying the Bragg relation, $2d \sin \theta = \lambda$, 2λ, 3λ, etc., are diffracted. (The distance between two lattice planes is d, and θ is the angle of incidence of the beam on these planes.) It is the same for electrons. If we consider for some specified direction of propagation three particular lattice planes (Fig. A.1), corresponding to spacings d_1, d_2, d_3, and angles of incidence θ_1, θ_2 and θ_3, we can foresee that $E(\mathbf{k})$ will be discontinuous for the corresponding $\mathbf{k}_1$, $\mathbf{k}_2$ and $\mathbf{k}_3$ values. Two cases may be considered (Fig. A.2), depending on whether the potential is more or less uniform (a, metallic crystals), or varies rapidly (b, iono-covalent crystals). In the first case the forbidden bands, corresponding to each of the chosen set of planes, only cover a narrow energy range so that forbidden energies do not occur simultaneously for the various lattice planes. In the second case, however, the range of

forbidden energies is large and their superposition still leaves a common
forbidden energy band.

This energy band scheme is the basis of mathematical techniques called

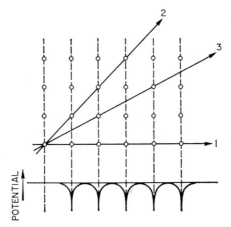

FIG. A.1. Traces for three typical lattice planes

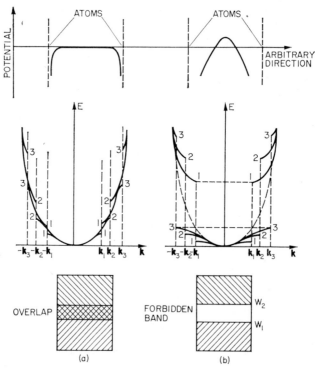

FIG. A.2. $E(\mathbf{k})$ function for two types of periodic potential 'band theory', which are useful for the study of germanium and silicon. Their application would be far more difficult for many of the problems considered in this book. Semiconducting solids naturally fall into the second class considered above: the electrons, bound to their atoms, fill all the available energy levels below W_1. They can only become free and contribute to conduction if they acquire an energy at least equal to the difference $E_G = W_1 - W_2$, called the energy gap (*énergie d'activation* or *largeur de bande interdite* in French literature) (Fig. A.3). This energy will be

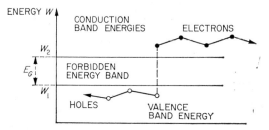

FIG. A.3. Intrinsic conductivity in band theory

acquired by an ever increasing number of electrons as the temperature is raised, since this will raise their thermal energy. One may show that in the absence of electrolytic conductivity, the so-called intrinsic conductivity follows a law:

$$\sigma = \sigma_0 \exp\left(-E_G/2kT\right)$$

where k is Boltzmann's constant ($8\cdot62 \times 10^{-5}$ eV/°K). Thus at low temperatures the number of free electrons is very small and the conductivity arises principally from the sort of mechanism discussed in Chapter 2 (vacancies, interstitials and impurities). These centres perturb the periodicity of the lattice and hence the conditions for propagation of the electrons and holes in their vicinity. In Fig. A.4 we represent these centres by inter-

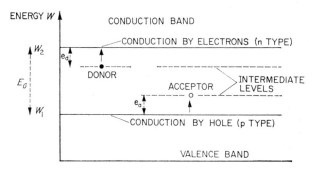

FIG. A.4. Extrinsic conductivity in band theory

mediate energy levels, shown as points, where conduction is not possible. The extrinsic conductivity due to these levels thus varies as

$$\sigma = \sigma_0 \exp\left(-e_d/kT\right)$$

where e_d (or e_a) represents the difference between the donor energy and W_2 (or the acceptor and W_1), and is often of the order of $E_G/10$ or $E_G/20$.

The exponential variation of conductivity

$$\sigma = Ne\,\mu$$

is generally due to the variation of N (or P), whose temperature dependence is shown schematically in Fig. A.5. The decrease in the mobility when the temperature is raised gives a curve for $\sigma\,(T)$ which differs slightly from that shown, and which displays a minimum between regions 2 and 3 (resistivity maximum). In contrast, certain materials display conductivities due to a hopping mechanism in which N varies only slightly with temperature. The exponential variation of σ is thus caused by a variation of the same form in μ. This is the case with many oxides and noticeably those compounds with valence induction described in Section 5.2.

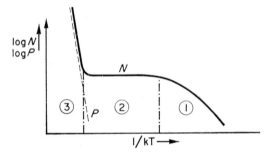

FIG. A.5. Number of free carriers as a function of temperature in the case $N > P$ (following AIGRAIN et al. [4])

In band theory the crystal structure becomes apparent via the consequent changes in the valence and conduction band levels, and hence in the height of the forbidden gap, when the propagation direction changes. The smallest value of E_G thus corresponds to the energy difference between the conduction band minimum and the valence band maximum, which may occur either for the same propagation direction (direct transitions) or for different ones (indirect transitions). The III V compounds are often of the first type, whilst Ge and Si are of the second type.

For more complete details of the ideas of band theory one may refer to the book by AIGRAIN and ENGLERT [4].

BIBLIOGRAPHY

[1] GOUDET, G. and MEULEAU, C. *Les Semiconducteurs*, Eyrolles, Paris, 1957 (Eng. trans. Macdonald, London, 1957).

[2] IOFFE, A. F. *Fizika Poluprovodnikov*, Akad. Nauk S.S.S.R., Moscow, 1957 (Eng. trans. Infosearch, London, 1960).

[3] KETELAAR, J. A. A. *Chemical Constitution*, Elsevier, Amsterdam, 1958.

[4] AIGRAIN, P. and ENGLERT, F. *Les Semiconducteurs*, Dunod, Paris, 1958 (Eng. trans. Methuen, London, to be published).

[5] SPENKE, E. *Electronische Halbleiter*, Springer, Berlin, 1958 (Eng. trans. McGraw-Hill, New York, 1958).

[6] HANNAY, O. *Semiconductors*, Reinhold, New York, 1959.

[7] BUBE, R. H. *Photoconductivity*, Wiley, New York, 1960.

[8] HILSUM, C. and ROSE-INNES, A. C. *Semiconducting* III-V *Compounds*, Pergamon Press, Oxford, 1961.

[9] IOFFE, A. F. and REGEL, A. R. *Progr. Semiconductors* **4,** 237 (ed. GIBSON), Heywood, London, 1960.

[10] WERNICK, J. H. and WOLFE, R. *Electronics* **33,** 103, 1960.

[1.1] PAULING, L. C. *The Nature of the Chemical Bond*, Cornell, Ithaca, 1960.

[1.2] EMELÉUS, H. J. and ANDERSON, J. S. *Modern Aspects of Inorganic Chemistry*, Routledge & Kegan Paul, London, 1952.

[1.3] ZINTL, E., GOUBEAU, J. and DULLENKOPF, W. *Z. phys. Chem.*, A **154,** 1, 1931.

[1.4] ZINTL, E. and KAISER, H. *Z. anorg. Chem.*, **211,** 113, 1933.

[1.5] HUME-ROTHERY, W. *The Structure of Metals and Alloys*, Inst. Metals, London, 1936.

[1.6] FAJANS, K. *Z. Krist.* **61,** 18, 1925.

[1.7] RICHTER, H., BERCKHEMER, H. and BREITLING, G. *Z. Naturf.* **9a,** 236, 1954.

[1.8] GAY, R. *Cours de Cristallographie*, I. Gauthier-Villars, Paris, 1958.

[1.9] SIDGWICK, N. V. and POWELL, H. M. *Proc. Roy. Soc. London*, A **176,** 153, 1940.

[1.10] WELLS, C. P. *Solid State Physics* (eds. SEITZ, F. and TURNBULL, D.), 7, 45, Academic Press, New York, 1958.

[1.11] MOOSER, E. and PEARSON, W. B. *Rep. Meeting Semiconductors* (Rugby, April, 1956), Phys. Soc.

[2.1] FRIEDEL, J. *Action des rayonnements de grande énèrgie sur les solides*, Gauthier-Villars, Paris, 1956.

[2.2] READ, W. T. Jr. *Dislocations in Crystals*, McGraw-Hill, New York, 1953.

[2.3] COTTRELL, A. H. *Dislocations and Plastic Flow*, Oxford, 1953.

[2.4] FRIEDEL, J. *Les Dislocations*, Gauthier-Villars, Paris, 1956.

[2.5] TAYLOR, G. I. *Proc. Roy. Soc. London*, A **145**, 362, 1934.

[2.6] OROWAN, E. *Z. Phys.* **89**, 634, 1934.

[2.7] FRANK, F. C. *Proc. Phys. Soc. London* A **62**, 131, 202, 1949.

[2.8] REES, A. L. G. *Chemistry of the Defect Solid State*, Methuen, London, 1954.

[2.9] POHL, R. *Phys. Z.* **39**, 36, 1939.

[2.10] SEITZ, F. *Rev. Mod. Phys.* **18**, 384, 1946.

[2.11] SEITZ, F. *Rev. Mod. Phys.* **26**, 7, 1954.

[2.12] SCHOTTKY, W. and WAGNER, C. *Z. phys. Chem.* B **11**, 163, 1930.

[2.13] KLEINSCHROD, F. G. *Ann. Phys.* **27**, 97, 1936.

[2.14] VARLEY, J. H. O. *J. Nucl. Energy* **1**, 130, 1954.

[2.15] SAINT-JAMES, D. *J. Phys. Radium* **18**, 260, 1956.

[2.16] SHOCKLEY, W. *Electrons and Holes in Semiconductors*, Van Nostrand, Princeton, 1950.

[2.17] SYRKIN, Y. K. and DYATKINA, M. E. *Structure of Molecules and the Chemical Bond*, Interscience, London, 1950.

[2.18] KREBS, H. *Physica* **20**, 1125, 1954.

[2.19] SUCHET, J. P. Proceedings of the International Conference on Semiconductor Physics (Prague, 1960), *Czech. J. Phys.* 904, 1961.

[2.20] SLATER, J. C. and KOSTER, G. F. *Phys. Rev.* **94**, 1498, 1954.

[2.21] CURIE, D. *Luminescence Crystalline*, Dunod, Paris, 1961.

[2.22] BRILL, R., GRIMM, H. G., HERMANN, C. and PETERS, C. *Ann. Phys.* **34**, 419, 1955.

[2.23] GUERON, M. *C. R. Acad. Sci. Paris* **254**, 1969, 1962, Thesis, Paris, 1964.

[2.24] GOODMAN, C. H. L. *Nature* **187**, 590, 1960.

[3.1] JOST, W. *Diffusion in Solids, Liquids and Gases*, Academic Press, New York, 1952.

[3.2] LE CLAIRE, A. D. *Progress in Metal Physics* **4**, Pergamon Press, Oxford, 1953.

[3.3] SEITH, W. *Diffusion in Metallen*, Springer, Berlin, 1955.

[3.4] SMITS, F. M. *Halbleiter u. Phosphore*, p. 329 (eds. SCHÖN, M. and WELKER, H.), Vieweg, Brunswick, 1958; and *Proc. IRE* **46**, 1049, 1958.

[3.5] BURCHENALL, C. E. *Mechanism of Diffusion in the Solid State*, Inst. Metals, London, 1960.

[3.6] FULLER, C. S. *Transistor Technology*, III, 64 (ed. BIONDI, F. J.), Van Nostrand, Princeton, 1958.

[3.7] TANENBAUM, M. and THOMAS, D. E. *RCA Rev.* **35**, 1, 1956.

[3.8] GERMAIN, J. E. *La Catalyse hétérogène*, Dunod, Paris, 1959.

[3.9] SIMON, J. and GERMAIN, J. E. *Cours de chimie*, I. Baillères, Paris, 1958.

[3.10] VON BAUMBACH, H. H. and WAGNER, C. *Z. phys. Chem.* B **22**, 199, 1933.

[3.11] REISS, H., FULLER, C. S. and MORIN, F. J. *Bell Syst. Tech. J.* **35**, 535, 1956.

[3.12] REISS, H. and FULLER, C. S. *J. Metals* **8**, 276, 1956.

[3.13] KAISER, W., FRISCH, H. L. and REISS, H. *Phys. Rev.* **112**, 1546, 1958.

[3.14] SUCHET, J. P. *J. Chim. Phys.* **58**, 455, 1961.

[3.15] KOVER, F. and QUILLIET, A. *C. R. Acad. Sci. Paris* **244**, 1739, 1957.

[3.16] HROSTOWSKI, H. J. and FULLER, C. S. *J. Phys. and Chem. Solids* **4**, 155, 1958.

[3.17] KRÖGER, F. A. and VINK, H. J. *Solid State Physics* **3**, 307 (eds. SEITZ, F. and TURNBULL, D.), Academic Press, New York, 1956.

[3.18] BROUWER, G. *Philips Res. Rep.* **9**, 366, 1954.

[3.19] KRÖGER, F. A., VINK, H. J. and VAN DEN BOOMGAARD, J. *Z. Phys.* **203**, 1, 1954; and *Z. phys. Chem.* **1**, 72, 1954.

[3.20] BLOEM, J. *Philips Res. Rep.* **11**, 273, 1956.

[3.21] SUCHET, J. P. *J. Phys. and Chem. Solids* **12**, 74, 1959.

[3.22] DRABBLE, J. R. and GOODMAN, C. H. L. *J. Phys. and Chem. Solids* **5**, 142, 1958.

[3.23] VLASOVA, R. M. and STIL'BANS, L. S. *Zh. Tekh. Fiz.* **25**, 569, 1955.

[3.24] RODOT, H. and BENEL, H. *Solid State Phys. Electr. Telecomm.* **1**, 692 (eds. DESIRANT, M. and MICHIELS, J. L.), Academic Press, London, 1960.

[3.25] BLAND, J. A. and BASINSKI, S. J. *Canad. J. Phys.* **39**, 1040, 1961.

[3.26] AUSTIN, I. G. and SHEARD, A. *J. Electronics* **3**, 236, 1957.

[3.27] SUCHET, J. P. *Acta Cryst.* **14**, 651, 1961.

[3.28] KREBS, H. *Acta Cryst.* **9**, 95, 1956.

[3.29] MIYAZAWA, H. and FUKUHARA, S. *J. Phys. Soc. Japan* **7**, 645, 1952.

[4.1] SUCHET, J. P. *J. Phys. and Chem. Solids* **12**, 74, 1959.

[4.2] KREBS, H. and SCHOTTKY, W. *Halbleiterprobleme* I, 25 (ed. SCHOTTKY, W.), Vieweg, Brunswick, 1954.

[4.3] KREBS, H. *Physica* **20**, 1125, 1954.

[4.4] KREBS, H. *Z. anorg. Chem.* **278**, 82, 1955.

[4.5] KREBS, H. *Acta Cryst.* **9**, 95, 1956.

[4.6] MOOSER, E. and PEARSON, W. B. *Rep. Meeting Semiconductors* (Rugby, 1956), Phys. Soc.

[4.7] MOOSER, E. and PEARSON, W. B. *J. Electronics* **1**, 629, 1956.

[4.8] MOOSER, E. and PEARSON, W. B. *J. Chem. Phys.* **26**, 893, 1957.

[4.9] HUME-ROTHERY, W. *The Structure of Metals and Alloys*, Inst. Metals, London, 1936.

[4.10] WELLS, C. P. *Solid State Physics* **7**, 45 (eds. SEITZ, F. and TURNBULL, D.), Academic Press, New York, 1958.

[4.11] RAYNOR, G. V. *Progr. Metal Phys.* **I**, 1 (ed. CHALMERS), Butterworths, London, 1949.

[4.12] SUCHET, J. P. *J. Phys. and Chem. Solids* **16**, 265, 1960.

[4.13] FIELDING, P., FISCHER, G. and MOOSER, E. *J. Phys. and Chem. Solids* **8**, 434, 1959.

[4.14] WARING, W., PITMAN, D. T. and STEELE, R. S. *J. Appl. Phys.* **29**, 1002, 1958.

[4.15] SOKOL'SKAIA, I. L. *Zh. Tekh. Fiz.* **27**, 127, 1957.

[4.16] SPICER, W. E. *J. Phys. and Chem. Solids* **8**, 437, 1959.

[4.17] MILLER, J. F., REID, F. J. and HIMES, R. C. *J. Electrochem. Soc.* **106**, 1043, 1959.

[4.18] PEARSON, W. B. *Canad. J. Phys.* **35**, 886, 1957.

[4.19] FISCHER, G. *Canad. J. Phys.* **36**, 1435, 1958.

[4.20] DUDKIN, L. D. *Zh. Tekh. Fiz.* **28**, 240, 1958.

[4.21] SUCHET, J. P. *Phys. Status Solidi* **2**, 167, 1962.

[5.1] SUCHET, J. P. *Bull. Soc. Fr. Électr.* **5**, 274, 1955.

[5.2] VERWEY, E. J. W. *Semiconducting Materials* (ed. HENISCH), Butterworths, London, 1951.

[5.3] FRIEDERICH, E. and SITTIG, L. *Z. anorg. Chem.* **145**, 127, 1925.

[5.4] BEVAN, D. J. M., SHELTON, J. P. and ANDERSON, J. S. *J. Chem. Soc. London* 1729, 1928.

[5.5] VERWEY, E. J. W. and DE BOER, J. H. *Recueils Trav. Chim. des Pays-Bas* **55**, 531, 1936.

[5.6] VERWEY, E. J. W., HAAYMAN, P. W., ROMEYN, F. C. and VAN OOSTERHOUT, G. W. *Philips Res. Rep.* **5**, 173, 1950.

[5.7] SUCHET, J. P. *J. Phys. Radium* **16**, 417, 1955.

[5.8] KOOPS, C. G. *Phys. Rev.* **83**, 121, 1951.

[5.9] SUCHET, J. P. *J. Phys. Radium* **18**, 10 A, 1957. (Cf. also *Proc. IRE* **45**, 360, 1957.)

[5.10] FORESTIER, H. *C. R. Acad. Sci. Paris* **192**, 842, 1931.

[5.11] SNOEK, J. L. *New Developments in Ferromagnetic Materials*, Elsevier, Amsterdam, 1947.

[5.12] NÉEL, L. *Ann. Phys.* **12**, 137, 1948.

[5.13] GUILLAUD, C. *J. Rech. C.N.R.S.* (Bellevue) **3**, 113, 1950–51.

[5.14] GORTER, E. W. *Thesis*, University of Leyden, 1954.

[5.15] GUILLAUD, C. *Proc. IRE*, Part B, **104**, 165, 1957.

[5.16] GUILLAUD, C., VILLERS, G., MARAIS, A. and PAULUS, M. *Solid State Phys. Electr. Telecomm.* **2**, 71 (eds. DESIRANT, M. and MICHIELS, J. L.), Academic Press, London, 1960.

[5.17] FAIRWEATHER, A. and FROST, E. J. *Proc. IEE* **100,** 15, 1953.

[5.18] VOLGER, J. *Physica* **20,** 49, 1954.

[5.19] PARKER, R. *Physica* **20,** 1314, 1954.

[5.20] WEBB, C. E. and FORD, L. H. *J. IEE* **75,** 787, 1934.

[5.21] SUCHET, J. P. *J. Chem. Phys.* **25,** 368, 1956.

[6.1] AIGRAIN, P. and BALKANSKI, M. *Table de constantes—Semiconducteurs,* Pergamon Press, Paris, 1961.

[6.2] IOFFE, A. F. *Izv. Akad. Nauk* (Fiz.) **15,** 477, 1951.

[6.3] BRAGG, W. L. *Phil. Mag.* **40,** 169, 1920.

[6.4] LANDÉ, A. *Z. Phys.* **1,** 191, 1920.

[6.5] WASASTJERNA, J. A. *Soc. Sci. Fenn. Comm. Phys. Math.* **38,** 1, 1923.

[6.6] GOLDSCHMIDT, V. M. *Skrifter Norske Videnskaps-Akad.,* Oslo, 1 Klasse, 1926.

[6.7] PAULING, L. C. *The Nature of the Chemical Bond,* Cornell, Ithaca, 1960.

[6.8] SUCHET, J. P. *J. Phys. and Chem. Solids* **16,** 265, 1960.

[6.9] SUCHET, J. P. *Acta Cryst.* **14,** 651, 1961.

[6.10] PAULING, L. C. *J. Amer. Chem. Soc.* **54,** 3570, 1932.

[6.11] HAISSINSKY, M. *J. Phys. Radium* **7,** 7, 1946.

[6.12] MULLIKEN, R. S. *J. Chem. Phys.* **2,** 782, 1934.

[6.13] GORDY, W. *J. Chem. Phys.* **14,** 305, 1946.

[6.14] GORDY, W. *Phys. Rev.* **69,** 604, 1946.

[6.15] PRITCHARD, H. O. and SKINNER, H. A. *Chem. Rev. Baltimore* **55,** 745, 1955.

[6.16] GORDY, W. and THOMAS, D. E. *J. Chem. Phys.* **24,** 439, 1956.

[6.17] HANNAY, N. B. and SMYTH, C. P. *J. Amer. Chem. Soc.* **68,** 171, 1946.

[6.18] ROBINSON, D. Z. *J. Chem. Phys.* **17,** 1022, 1949.

[6.19] GOODMAN, C. H. L. *J. Electronics* **1,** 115, 1955.

[6.20] WELKER, H. *Z. Naturf.* A **7,** 744, 1952.

[6.21] WELKER, H. *Solid State Phys. Electr. Telecomm.* **2,** 645 (eds. DESIRANT, M. and MICHIELS, J. L.), Academic Press, New York, 1960.

[6.22] PEARSON, W. B. *Canad. J. Chem.* **37,** 1191, 1959.

[6.23] MOOSER, E. and PEARSON, W. B. *Acta Cryst.* **12,** 1015, 1959.

[6.24] ORMONT, B. F. *Dokl. Akad. Nauk S.S.S.R* **124,** 129, 1959.

[6.25] MANCA, P. *J. Phys. and Chem. Solids* **20,** 268, 1961.

[6.26] BÖTTCHER, C. J. F. *Recueils Trav. Chim. des Pays-Bas* **65,** 19, 1946.

[6.27] SUCHET, J. P. *J. Phys. and Chem. Solids* **21,** 156, 1961.

[6.28] FOLBERTH, O. G. *Z. Naturf.* A **13,** 756, 1958.

[6.29] SLATER, J. C. and KOSTER, G. F. *Phys. Rev.* **94,** 1498, 1954.

[6.30] RUPPEL, W., ROSE, A. and GERRITSEN, H. J. *Helv. Phys. Acta* **30,** 238, 1957.

[6.31] ZHUZE, V. P. *Zh. Tekh. Fiz.* **25**, 2079, 1955.

[7.1] SUCHET, J. P. *Thèse d'État*, Paris, 1961.

[7.2] SUCHET, J. P. Proceedings of the International Conference on Semiconductor Physics (Prague, 1960), *Czech. J. Phys.* 904, 1961.

[7.3] SUCHET, J. P. *J. Phys. and Chem. Solids* **21**, 156, 1961.

[7.4] HAHN, H., FRANK, F. C., KLINGLER, W., MEYER, A. D. and STÖRGER, G. *Z. anorg. Chem.* **271**, 153, 1953.

[7.5] KOLOMIETS, B. T. and GORIUNOVA, N. A. *Zh. Tekh. Fiz.* **25**, 984, 1955.

[7.6] WERNICK, J. H. and BENSON, K. E. *J. Phys. and Chem. Solids* **3**, 157, 1957.

[7.7] GLAZOV, V. M., MIRGALOVSKAYA, M. S. and PETRAKOVA, L. A. *Izv. Akad. Nauk S.S.S.R* **10**, 68, 1957.

[7.8] SUCHET, J. P. *C. R. Acad. Sci. Paris* **225**, 1444, 1962.

[7.9] PRITCHARD, H. O. and SKINNER, H. A. *Chem. Rev. Baltimore* **55**, 745, 1955.

[7.10] SUCHET, J. P. Proceedings of the International Conference on the Physics of Semiconductors (Exeter, 1962), 790, 1963.

[7.11] SUCHET, J. P., RODOT, M., LEROUX-HUGON, P. and RODOT, H. *Adv. Energy Conv.* **3**, 569, 1963.

[7.12] ALBERS, W., HAAS, C. and VAN DER MAESEN, F. *J. Phys. and Chem. Solids* **15**, 306, 1960.

[7.13] ALLGAIER, R. S. and SCHEIE, P. O. *Bull. Amer. Phys. Soc.* **6**, 436, 1961.

[7.14] HEIKES, R. R. and URE, R. W. *Thermoelectricity*, Interscience, New York, 1961.

[7.15] LEROUX-HUGON, P., RODOT, M. and SUCHET, J. P. *C. R. Acad. Sci. Paris* **254**, 1250, 1962.

[7.16] ERTL, M. E., HAZELDEN, D. W. and GOLDSMID, H. J. Proceedings of the International Conference on the Physics of Semiconductors (Exeter, 1962), 777, 1963.

[7.17] LINDBERG, O. *Proc. IRE* **40**, 1414, 1952.

[7.18] SPITZER, W. G., WERNICK, J. H. and WOLFE, R. *Sol. State Electr.* **7**, 96, 1961.

[7.19] IOFFE, A. F. *Semiconductor Thermoelements and Thermoelectric Cooling*, Infosearch, London, 1957.

[7.20] RODOT, H. *C. R. Acad. Sci. Paris* **249**, 1872, 1959.

[7.21] FLEISCHMANN, H., FOLBERTH, O. G. and PFISTER, H. *Z. Naturf.* A **14**, 999, 1959.

[8.1] BATES, L. F. *Modern Magnetism*, Univ. Press, Cambridge, 1951.

[8.2] SUCHET, J. P. *Physica Status Solidi* **2**, 167, 1962.

[8.3] PAULING, L. C. *The Nature of the Chemical Bond*, Cornell, Ithaca, 1960.

[8.4] HARALDSEN, H. *16th Congr. Inter. Chim. Pure Appl.* (Paris, 1957), Birkhäuser, Basle, 1957.

[8.5] PEARSON, W. B. *Canad. J. Phys.* **35**, 886, 1957.

[8.6] HULLIGER, F. *Helv. Phys. Acta* **32**, 615, 1959.

[8.7] DUDKIN, L. D. *Dokl. Akad. Nauk S.S.S.R* **127**, 1203, 1959.

[8.8] DUDKIN, L. D. *Fiz. Tv. Tela* **2**, 397, 1960.

[8.9] BOKII, G. B. *Introduction to Crystallography* (in Russian), Moscow, 1954.

[8.10] DUDKIN, L. D. and VAÏDANICH, V. I. *Fiz. Tv. Tela* **2**, 1526, 1960.

[8.11] FOËX, G., GORTER, E. W. and SMITS, F. M. *Constantes magnétiques selectionnées*, Masson, Paris, 1957.

[8.12] TSUBOKAWA, I. *J. Phys. Soc. Japan* **14**, 196, 1959.

[8.13] ADACHI, K. *J. Phys. Soc. Japan* **16**, 2187, 1961.

[8.14] SUCHET, J. P. *C. R. Acad. Sci. Paris* **255**, 2080, 1962.

[8.15] ORGEL, L. E. *An Introduction to Transition-Metal Chemistry*, Methuen, London, 1960.

[8.16] SUCHET, J. P. *J. Phys. Radium* **23**, 487, 1962.

[8.17] KRAMERS, H. A. *Physica* **1**, 182, 1934.

[8.18] ANDERSON, P. W. *Phys. Rev.* **79**, 350, 1950.

[8.19] SUCHET, J. P. *C. R. Acad. Sci. Paris* **253**, 2490, 1961.

[8.20] WOLLAN, E. O., KOEHLER, W. C. and WILKINSON, M. K. *Phys. Rev.* **110**, 638, 1958.

[8.21] HEIKES, R. R. *Phys. Rev.* **99**, 1232, 1955.

[8.22] FISCHER, G. and PEARSON, W. B. *Canad. J. Phys.* **36**, 1010, 1958.

[8.23] SUZUOKA, T. *J. Phys. Soc. Japan* **12**, 1344, 1957.

[8.24] UCHIDA, E., KONDOH, H. and FUKUOKA, N. *J. Phys. Soc. Japan* **11**, 27, 1956.

[8.25] VOLGER, J. *Semiconducting Materials* (ed. HENISCH), Butterworths, London, 162, 1951.

[8.26] HEIKES, R. R. *J. Appl. Phys.* **32**, Suppl. 2202, 1961.

[8.27] COLES, B. R. *Adv. Phys.* **7**, 40, 1958.

[8.28] FRIEDEL, J. and DE GENNES, P. *J. Phys. and Chem. Solids* **4**, 71, 1958.

[8.29] WEISS, R. J. and MAROTTA, A. S. *J. Phys. and Chem. Solids* **9**, 302, 1959.

[8.30] BUSCH, G., JUNOD, P., RISI, M. and VOGT, O. Proceedings of the International Conference on the Physics of Semiconductors (Exeter, 1962), 727, 1963.

[8.31] SUCHET, J. P. *C. R. Acad. Sci. Paris* **256**, 2563, 1963.

[8.32] KIEU VAN CON and SUCHET, J. P. *C. R. Acad. Sci. Paris* **256**, 2823, 1963.

[8.33] SMART, J. S. *Phys. Rev.* **86**, 968, 1952.

[8.34] ELLIOTT, N., CORLISS, L. and HASTINGS, J. *16ᵉ Congr. Inter. Chim. Pure Appl.* (Paris, 1957), Birkhäuser, Basle, 1957.

[9.1] RIEHL, N. V. *Zh. Fiz. Khim.* **6**, 959, 1955.

[9.2] POCCHETTINO, A. *Atti Acad. Lincei Rendiconti* **15** (1), 355, 1906.

[9.3] VARTANYAN, A. I. *Zh. Fiz. Khim.* **22**, 201, 1947.

[9.4] ELEY, D. D. *Nature* **162**, 819, 1948.

[9.5] VARTANYAN, A. I. *Zh. Fiz. Khim.* **22**, 769, 1948.

[9.6] METTE, H. and PICK, H. *Z. Phys.* **134**, 566, 1953.

[9.7] INOKUCHI, H. *Bull. Chem. Soc. Japan* **29**, 131, 1956.

[9.8] PICK, H. and WISSMAN, W. *Z. Phys.* **138**, 436, 1954.

[9.9] BREE, A., CARSWELL, D. J. and LYONS, L. E. *J. Chem. Soc. London* 1728, 1955.

[9.10] NORTHROP, D. C. and SIMPSON, O. *Proc. Roy. Soc. London* A **244**, 377, 1958.

[9.11] CURIE, D. *Luminescence cristalline*, Dunod, Paris, 1960.

[9.12] ELEY, D. D. and PARFITT, G. D. *Trans. Faraday Soc.* **51**, 1529, 1955.

[9.13] LONDON, F. *J. Phys.* **8**, 397, 1937.

[9.14] SZENT-GYÖRGYI, A. *Science* **93**, 609, 1941.

[9.15] NELSON, R. C. *J. Chem. Phys.* **27**, 864, 1957.

[9.16] INOKUCHI, H. *Bull. Chem. Soc. Japan* **24**, 222, 1951.

[9.17] ELEY, D. D. *Research* **12**, 293, 1959.

[9.18] ELEY, D. D., PARFITT, G. D., PERRY, M. G. and TAYSUM, D. H. *Trans. Faraday Soc.* **49**, 79, 1953.

[9.19] HOLMES-WALKER, W. A. and UBBELOHDE, A. R. J. P. *J. Chem. Soc. London* 720, 1954.

[9.20] McDONNEL, F. R. M., PINK, R. C. and UBBELOHDE, A. R. J. P. *J. Chem. Soc. London* 191, 1951.

[9.21] AKAMATU, H., INOKUCHI, H. and MATSUNAGA, Y. *Nature* **173**, 168, 1954.

[9.22] AKAMATU, H., INOKUCHI, H. and MATSUNAGA, Y. *Bull. Chem. Soc. Japan* **29**, 213, 1956.

[9.23] SLOUGH, W. and UBBELOHDE, A. R. J. P. *J. Chem. Soc. London* 982, 1957.

[9.24] ELEY, D. D. and INOKUCHI, H. *Proc. 3rd Biennial Carbon Conf.* (Buffalo, 1957), Pergamon Press, 1959.

[9.25] LABES, M. H., SEHR, R. and BOSE, M. *J. Chem. Phys.* **32**, 1570, 1960.

[9.26] GARRETT, C. G. B. Proceedings of the International Conference on Semiconductor Physics (Prague, 1960), *Czech. J. Phys.* 844, 1961.

[9.27] WINSLOW, F. H., PAPE, N. R. and MATTREYEK, W. *J. Polymer Science* **16**, 101, 1955.

[9.28] TOPTCHIEV, A. V., GEIDERIX, M. A., DAVIDOV, D. E., KARGIN, V. A., KRENTSEL, B. A., KOUSTANOVITCH, I. M. and POLAK, L. C. *Dokl. Akad. Nauk S.S.S.R.* **128**, 312, 1959.

AUTHOR INDEX

187

FORMULAE INDEX

191

SUBJECT INDEX